MERCURY IN THE UNITED STATES

DEMAND, SUPPLY AND USE CHANGES AND THE EPA'S ROADMAP FOR REDUCTION

ENVIRONMENTAL HEALTH - PHYSICAL, CHEMICAL AND BIOLOGICAL FACTORS

Additional books in this series can be found on Nova's website under the Series tab.

Additional e-books in this series can be found on Nova's website under the e-book tab.

MERCURY IN THE UNITED STATES

DEMAND, SUPPLY AND USE CHANGES AND THE EPA'S ROADMAP FOR REDUCTION

ERICA O. GOSSELIN
EDITOR

New York

Copyright © 2014 by Nova Science Publishers, Inc.

For permission to use material from this book please contact us:
Telephone 631-231-7269; Fax 631-231-8175
Web Site: http://www.novapublishers.com

NOTICE TO THE READER

The Publisher has taken reasonable care in the preparation of this book, but makes no expressed or implied warranty of any kind and assumes no responsibility for any errors or omissions. No liability is assumed for incidental or consequential damages in connection with or arising out of information contained in this book. The Publisher shall not be liable for any special, consequential, or exemplary damages resulting, in whole or in part, from the readers' use of, or reliance upon, this material. Any parts of this book based on government reports are so indicated and copyright is claimed for those parts to the extent applicable to compilations of such works.

Independent verification should be sought for any data, advice or recommendations contained in this book. In addition, no responsibility is assumed by the publisher for any injury and/or damage to persons or property arising from any methods, products, instructions, ideas or otherwise contained in this publication.

This publication is designed to provide accurate and authoritative information with regard to the subject matter covered herein. It is sold with the clear understanding that the Publisher is not engaged in rendering legal or any other professional services. If legal or any other expert assistance is required, the services of a competent person should be sought. FROM A DECLARATION OF PARTICIPANTS JOINTLY ADOPTED BY A COMMITTEE OF THE AMERICAN BAR ASSOCIATION AND A COMMITTEE OF PUBLISHERS.

Additional color graphics may be available in the e-book version of this book.

Library of Congress Cataloging-in-Publication Data

ISBN: 978-1-63117-592-3

Published by Nova Science Publishers, Inc. † New York

CONTENTS

PREFACE

Environmental concerns have led to numerous regulations that have dramatically decreased the reported production and use of mercury in the United States since the 1980s. Government legislation and subsequent industry actions have led to increased collection of mercury-containing materials and the recovery of mercury through recycling. Mercury emissions have been reduced and effective alternatives to mercury products have been developed for many applications. This book updates and quantifies the changes in demand, supply, use, and material flow for mercury in various sectors in the United States that have taken place since 1996.

Chapter 1 – Environmental concerns have led to numerous regulations that have dramatically decreased the reported production and use of mercury in the United States since the 1980s. Government legislation and subsequent industry actions have led to increased collection of mercury-containing materials and the recovery of mercury through recycling. Mercury emissions have been reduced and effective alternatives to mercury products have been developed for many applications. This study updates and quantifies the changes in demand, supply, use, and material flow for mercury in various sectors in the United States that have taken place since 1996.

Nearly all primary mercury produced in the United States is derived as a byproduct of processing of gold and silver ore in Nevada. Since 2001, annual production of mercury from gold and silver mining in Nevada has decreased by 22 percent overall because ore from greater depths containing low grade mercury is recovered, and mercury emissions from this source have decreased by 95 percent as a result of increased regulation and improved collection and suppression technology.

The distribution of consumption of mercury in the United States has changed as a result of regulation (elimination of large-scale mercury use in the paint and battery sectors), reduction by consumers (decommissioning of mercury-cell chloralkali manufacturing capacity), and technological advances (improvements in dental, lighting, and electrical and electronic sectors).

Mercury use in the chloralkali sector, the leading end-use sector in the United States in 1996, has declined by 98 percent from 136 metric tons (t) in 1996 to about 0.3 t in 2010 because of increased processing and recycling efficiencies and plant closures or conversion to other technologies. As plants were closed, mercury recovered from the infrastructure of decommissioned plants has been exported, making the United States a net exporter of mercury, even though no mercury has been produced as the primary product from mines in the United States since 1992.

In 1996, the three leading end-use sectors for mercury in the United States were chloralkali manufacturing (accounting for 38 percent of consumption), electrical and electronic instrumentation (13 percent of consumption), and instruments and measuring devices (11 percent of consumption). In 2010, the three leading end-use sectors were dental amalgam (accounting for between 35 and 57 percent of consumption), electrical and electronic instrumentation (29 percent of consumption), and batteries (8 percent of consumption). Mercury use in lighting is increasing because incandescent lights are being phased out in favor of mercury-containing compact fluorescent bulbs, but the demand for mercury per unit produced is small.

Dental amalgam constituted the largest amount of mercury in use in the United States. One study reported about 290 t of mercury in dental amalgam was estimated to be contained in human mouths, an estimated 30 t of mercury amalgam was treated as waste, 28.5 t of mercury amalgam was released to the environment, 6 t of amalgam was recycled, and 3.5 t was treated and stored in landfills in 2009.

Mercury contained in products recovered by State, municipal, or industry collection activities is recycled, but the estimated overall recycling rate is less than 10 percent. Increasingly, the U.S. mercury recycling industry has been processing a significant amount of mercury-containing material derived from foreign gold mining operations or decommissioned mercury-cell chloralkali plants.

Regulation of mercury export and storage is expected to result in surplus mercury inventories in the United States. The Mercury Export Ban Act of 2008 limits elemental mercury exports for unregulated uses such as artisanal gold mining after January 1, 2013, and requires development of adequate long-term storage facilities in the United States for elemental mercury. During the past 4 years, producers and recyclers of elemental mercury have been exporting large quantities of mercury in anticipation of this regulation, but the U.S. inventory of mercury in 2010 was estimated to have exceeded 7,000 t from Government stockpiles and industry stocks. Costs attributed to long-term storage may affect the competitiveness of mercury recycling.

Chapter 2 – Mercury is a naturally occurring element. It enters the environment as a result of natural sources (such as volcanoes) and human activities (such as industrial combustion and mining). Mercury is widespread in the U.S. and global environment. Human activities have increased the amount of mercury that is available in the atmosphere; in soils and sediments; and in lakes, streams, and oceans.

Significant progress has been made to date to reduce industrial emissions of mercury in the U.S., as well as to reduce or eliminate the amount of mercury used in various processes and products. Most of the large industrial sources of mercury emissions are sites where mercury is emitted as a byproduct of combustion processes. Other major sources of mercury include industrial processes and products that use mercury deliberately, such as certain chlor-alkali chlorine manufacturing processes, batteries, lamps, and measuring devices such as thermometers. Mercury is also released through mining practices, sewage discharge, and metal refining operations. When mercury is used in a product, most releases occur during manufacturing or disposal. In the U.S., there are over 100 manufacturing processes that use some form of mercury.

While elemental mercury is toxic to humans when it is ingested or inhaled, EPA is most concerned about methylmercury, as it is a potent form of mercury and it is the form to which humans primarily are exposed. Methylmercury can be formed from other deposited mercury by microbial action in sediment and soils. Once formed, methylmercury can be taken up by aquatic organisms and bioaccumulates up the aquatic food web. While all forms of mercury can bioaccumulate, methylmercury generally accumulates to a greater extent than other forms of mercury.

Over the past decade, addressing mercury risks to the environment and human health has been a focus for EPA. International, national, and local efforts to reduce mercury releases and uses have grown and are yielding impressive results. For example, overall U.S. mercury air emissions have been reduced by 45 percent since 1990, and mercury use in products and processes decreased 83 percent between 1980 and 1997. In 1997, U.S. man-made emissions contributed to approximately 3 percent of the global mercury pool.

In 1998, EPA issued a draft *Mercury Action Plan* for public comment as part of its effort to address priority persistent and bioaccumulative toxic pollutants. The Agency received extensive comments on the 1998 draft and held subsequent meetings with states and tribes, municipalities, industry, and environmental groups, including a series of "listening sessions" in 2003. Stakeholders provided very useful input on those aspects of the mercury issue on which they believed the Agency should focus its efforts. EPA also created an agency-wide workgroup to develop a new action plan, now called *EPA's Roadmap for Mercury (Roadmap)*.

Major offices at EPA are continuing to work to better understand the sources of mercury and how it impacts human health and the environment. The *Roadmap* describes the Agency's most important actions to reduce both mercury releases and human exposure to mercury. Creating the *Roadmap* has enabled the Agency to maximize coordination of its many diverse efforts, with the goal of improving EPA's mercury program. In addition to providing a roadmap for EPA, this report provides important information about mercury to other federal agencies, to our partners in state, tribal, and local governments, and to the public.

In: Mercury in the United States
Editor: Erica O. Gosselin

ISBN: 978-1-63117-592-3
© 2014 Nova Science Publishers, Inc.

Chapter 1

CHANGING PATTERNS IN THE USE, RECYCLING, AND MATERIAL SUBSTITUTION OF MERCURY IN THE UNITED STATES[*]

David R. Wilburn

ABBREVIATIONS

ABS	antilock brake
ALMR	Association of Lighting and Mercury Recyclers
BAT	best available technology
CFL	compact fluorescent lamp
DOE	U.S. Department of Energy
ECOS	Environmental Council of States
EPA	U.S. Environmental Protection Agency
FDA	U.S. Food and Drug Administration
GSFL	general service fluorescent lamp
HID	high-intensity discharge
IMERC	Interstate Mercury Education and Reduction Clearinghouse
LCD	liquid-crystal display
LED	light-emitting diode

[*] This is an edited, reformatted and augmented version of U.S. Geological Survey Scientific Investigations Report 2013–5137, dated 2013.

MCRBMA	Mercury Containing and Rechargeable Battery Management Act
MEBA	Mercury Export Ban Act of 2008
NDS	National Defense Stockpile
NEMA	National Electrical Manufacturers Association
NEWMOA	Northeast Waste Management Officials Association
NIST	National Institute of Standards and Technology
NVMSRP	National Vehicle Mercury Switch Recovery Program
ppm	parts per million
RCRA	Resource Conservation and Recovery Act
TCLP	toxicity characteristic leaching procedure
TRC	Thermostat Recycling Corporation
UNEP	United Nations Environment Programme
USGS	U.S. Geological Survey

ABSTRACT

Environmental concerns have led to numerous regulations that have dramatically decreased the reported production and use of mercury in the United States since the 1980s. Government legislation and subsequent industry actions have led to increased collection of mercury-containing materials and the recovery of mercury through recycling. Mercury emissions have been reduced and effective alternatives to mercury products have been developed for many applications. This study updates and quantifies the changes in demand, supply, use, and material flow for mercury in various sectors in the United States that have taken place since 1996.

Nearly all primary mercury produced in the United States is derived as a byproduct of processing of gold and silver ore in Nevada. Since 2001, annual production of mercury from gold and silver mining in Nevada has decreased by 22 percent overall because ore from greater depths containing low grade mercury is recovered, and mercury emissions from this source have decreased by 95 percent as a result of increased regulation and improved collection and suppression technology.

The distribution of consumption of mercury in the United States has changed as a result of regulation (elimination of large-scale mercury use in the paint and battery sectors), reduction by consumers (decommissioning of mercury-cell chloralkali manufacturing capacity), and technological advances (improvements in dental, lighting, and electrical and electronic sectors).

Mercury use in the chloralkali sector, the leading end-use sector in the United States in 1996, has declined by 98 percent from 136 metric tons (t) in 1996 to about 0.3 t in 2010 because of increased processing and recycling efficiencies and plant closures or conversion to other technologies. As plants were closed, mercury recovered from the infrastructure of decommissioned plants has been exported, making the United States a net exporter of mercury, even though no mercury has been produced as the primary product from mines in the United States since 1992.

In 1996, the three leading end-use sectors for mercury in the United States were chloralkali manufacturing (accounting for 38 percent of consumption), electrical and electronic instrumentation (13 percent of consumption), and instruments and measuring devices (11 percent of consumption). In 2010, the three leading end-use sectors were dental amalgam (accounting for between 35 and 57 percent of consumption), electrical and electronic instrumentation (29 percent of consumption), and batteries (8 percent of consumption). Mercury use in lighting is increasing because incandescent lights are being phased out in favor of mercury-containing compact fluorescent bulbs, but the demand for mercury per unit produced is small.

Dental amalgam constituted the largest amount of mercury in use in the United States. One study reported about 290 t of mercury in dental amalgam was estimated to be contained in human mouths, an estimated 30 t of mercury amalgam was treated as waste, 28.5 t of mercury amalgam was released to the environment, 6 t of amalgam was recycled, and 3.5 t was treated and stored in landfills in 2009.

Mercury contained in products recovered by State, municipal, or industry collection activities is recycled, but the estimated overall recycling rate is less than 10 percent. Increasingly, the U.S. mercury recycling industry has been processing a significant amount of mercury-containing material derived from foreign gold mining operations or decommissioned mercury-cell chloralkali plants.

Regulation of mercury export and storage is expected to result in surplus mercury inventories in the United States. The Mercury Export Ban Act of 2008 limits elemental mercury exports for unregulated uses such as artisanal gold mining after January 1, 2013, and requires development of adequate long-term storage facilities in the United States for elemental mercury. During the past 4 years, producers and recyclers of elemental mercury have been exporting large quantities of mercury in anticipation of this regulation, but the U.S. inventory of mercury in 2010 was estimated to have exceeded 7,000 t from Government stockpiles and industry stocks. Costs attributed to long-term storage may affect the competitiveness of mercury recycling.

INTRODUCTION

Mercury and its compounds have a long history of human use, dating back about 3,500 years in Egypt. Mercury is the only metal that is liquid at room temperature (20 degrees Celsius). It is a good electrical conductor, is highly resistant to corrosion, and has a high charge-density-to-weight ratio. The volatility of mercury at relatively low temperatures permits the metal to be readily separated from other materials through the application of heat and to be recovered with few impurities. Mercury has been used in a wide variety of applications, including batteries, catalysts, chloralkali production, dental amalgams, electrical switches and relays, electrochemistry, explosives, flow meters, fungicides, gold recovery, preservatives, reagents, thermometers, and thermostats (Sznopek and Goonan, 2000).

Although the high solubility of mercury in water as methylmercury and the ease of vaporization of methylmercury can be an advantage in some applications, these properties make mercury very mobile in the environment. Atmospheric releases of mercury vapor can be carried large distances and be deposited into lakes and streams. Under anaerobic conditions, mercury is converted into methylmercury, an organic form of mercury, which has been proven to be a neurotoxin that is easily bioaccumulated organisms (Griesbauer, 2007). Methylmercury can enter the food chain and accumulate in fish tissues at levels that can endanger animal and human populations further up the food chain.

Management and regulatory responses to environmental problems that are possibly related to mercury were initially constrained by a lack of reliable information on biological significance, chemical interaction with the environment, methods of transport, and manmade sources. Research advances since the 1980s have allowed scientists to assess the level of mercury in the environment; the data from these assessments have provided the baselines to develop regulatory actions and voluntary controls. Government legislation and industry actions have resulted in a reduction in the production and use of mercury since the late 1980s and an increase in the recovery of mercury through recycling. Research in recent years has led to improved mercury emissions collection technology and development of cost-effective alternatives to mercury-bearing products for many applications.

Materials flow studies provide insights into the factors that affect the flow of materials and quantify the amount of these materials from one form or location to another. Such studies provide background information for decisionmakers when balancing or weighing competing interests, managing resources, or formulating policy. A materials flow study of mercury in the United States was last published by the U.S. Geological Survey (USGS) in 2000 and contained data as of 1996. A mercury recycling study was published by the USGS in 2005 using data as of 2000. This report, though not a global materials flow study or comprehensive recycling study, updates and quantifies the changes in use and flows of mercury that took place in the United States since 1996 in response to perceived health risks of mercury and consequent Government regulation. The report also identifies recurrent recycling activities and, where possible, quantifies the amount of mercury recycling that is taking place in the United States by end-use application. Factors influencing the magnitude of recycling also are discussed. The report identifies significant sources and stocks of mercury and discusses uses where significant substitution is taking place. The report evaluates industry use of mercury in light of existing and planned regulatory framework and assesses the possible effects of legislation on material use. The methodology used for this report is similar to that used in the Matos and Brooks (2005).

Because the report focuses on nonfuel mineral sources, it does not include mercury flows from coal-burning power-plants. Coal accounts for about half of the total U.S. manmade mercury emissions (U.S. Environmental Protection Agency, 2012e). About 75 metric tons (t) of mercury is burned in coal consumed at powerplants in the United States, and about 25 t of mercury is captured through pollution control equipment (Bowen and Irwin, 2007). In November 2012, the U.S. Environmental Protection Agency (EPA) proposed updated emission limits for new powerplants (U.S. Environmental Protection Agency, 2012b).

HISTORICAL USE, PRODUCTION, AND LEGISLATION OF MERCURY

Changes that have taken place in the primary and secondary (recycled) mercury industry in the United States reflect concern over the effects of mercury on the environment and human health and the resulting Federal and State regulatory actions implemented to reduce contamination of the environment from manmade mercury sources and to limit the use, export, and disposal of mercury. Figure 1 illustrates consumption, production, stocks, and prices of mercury in the United States from 1971 through 2010; significant Federal legislative and regulatory action from 1970 through 2011 is listed in table 1.

A number of States have implemented regulatory actions related to production, emissions, use, transport, and disposal of mercury. In the 1960s, strong demand for mercury in batteries, chloralkali manufacturing, and as a paint additive coupled with a relatively limited supply resulted in high mercury prices. However, after mercury was designated a toxic pollutant in 1971, regulations were promulgated to reduce mercury emissions and use. Demand for mercury subsequently decreased, resulting in a decrease in the price of mercury.

As shown in figure 1, the price of mercury in 1998 constant dollars generally decreased from 1971 through 2001 and increased from 2001 through 2010, although there was a large fluctuation in price from 1974 through 1980. The greatest increase in mercury price since 1971 took place from 2009 to 2010. Impending mercury export bans in the European Union (2011) and the United States (2013) in combination with rising gold and silver prices have affected the price of mercury. Mercury is used in small-scale artisanal gold mining in many parts of the world, and the rising price of gold has influenced the global demand for mercury (Brooks, 2012). Many artisanal gold deposits contain a significant amount of silver; the greater the amount of silver present in the deposit, the more mercury is required to recover the gold (Artisanal Gold Council, 2011). The price of mercury was also affected by diminishing supplies of mercury recycled from end-of-use mercury-containing products and limited availability of mercury from China and Kyrgyzstan (Brooks, 2012).

No mines have produced mercury as a principal product in the United States since the McDermitt Mine in northern Nevada closed in 1992 (Brooks, 2012). The largest production of byproduct mercury took place at several precious metal mines in Nevada in 2010, although mercury may be recovered in other areas such as base metal mines in Alaska (Red Dog Mine) and New York (Balmat district). Much of the base metal ore mined in Alaska is processed in Canada, and mercury production statistics are not available. In 2010, byproduct mercury production in the United States was estimated to be about 92 t. Since the early 1970s, annual demand for mercury in the United States has declined from about 2,000 t (U.S. Bureau of Mines, 1973–96; U.S. Geological Survey, 1997–2011) to an estimated 70 t in 2010.

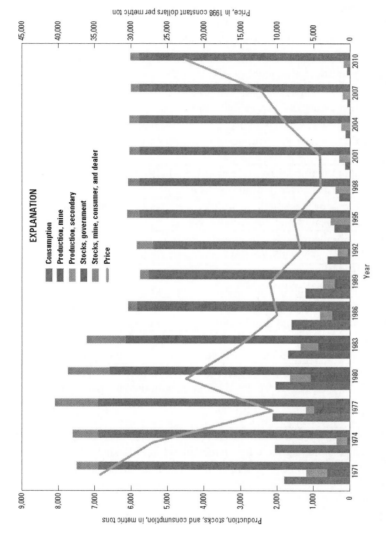

Figure 1. Mercury production, consumption, stocks, and prices from 1971 through 2010 in the United States. Secondary production includes byproduct production from gold, recycled material, and sales from Government stockpiles before 1994. Data are from U.S. Bureau of Mines (1973–96) and U.S. Geological Survey (1997–2011, 2012). Prices in constant 1998 dollars are from U.S. Geological Survey (2012).

Table 1. Federal legislation governing mercury in the United States

Year	Legislation
1970	The Clean Air Act authorized the U.S. Environmental Protection Agency (EPA) to set national standards for hazardous air pollutants.
1971	Mercury designated as a hazardous pollutant.
1972	The Federal Insecticide, Fungicide, Rodenticide Act prohibited the use of many pesticides containing mercury.
1972	The Federal Water Pollution Control Act authorized the EPA to regulate mercury discharges into waterways.
1973	The Mercury was designated as a toxic pollutant. Standards were enacted for mercury ore-processing facilities and chloralkali plants.
1974	The Safe Drinking Water Act authorized the EPA to set standards for hazardous substances in drinking water.
1978	The Resource Conservation and Recovery Act established regulations for the disposal of mercury-bearing waste.
1980	The Comprehensive, Environmental Response, Compensation, and Liability Act enacted Superfund to clean toxic waste sites.
1992	The EPA banned land disposal of high mercury content wastes generated from chloralkali plants.
1993	The EPA canceled registrations of the last two mercury-containing fungicides at the request of manufacturers.
1994	Congress suspended mercury sales from National Defense Stockpile until environmental issues resolved.
1996	The Mercury-Containing and Rechargeable Battery Management Act prohibited the sales of regulated batteries without recyclability or disposal labels and phased out most batteries containing intentionally added mercury.
2000	The EPA announced ban on discharges of various bioaccumulative chemicals, including mercury, in the Great Lakes Basin.
2002	The EPA set a limit of 2 parts per billion mercury in drinking water. The U.S. Food and Drug Administration (FDA) set a limit of 1 part per million of methylmercury in seafood. The Occupational Safety and Health Administration (OSHA) set a limit of 0.05 milligram per cubic meter of mercury in workplace air.
2002	The EPA banned the sale of mercury-containing thermometers.
2003	The Omnibus Mercury Emissions Reduction Act mandated reduced mercury emissions from all major sources, directed the EPA to issue revised standards, and set a timetable for the reduction of mercury emissions.

Year	Legislation
2007	The Energy Independence and Security Act included provisions phasing out incandescent light bulbs in favor of energy-efficient, compact fluorescent lights (CFLs), which contain mercury.
2008	The Mercury Export Ban Act prohibited the export of mercury after January 1, 2013, sale and transfer of elemental mercury, and addressed long term storage of elemental mercury.
2010	The EPA issued new rule under the Toxic Substances Control Act to be notified at least 90 days before the beginning of production of mercury-containing devices (such as flow meters, natural gas manometers, and pyrometers) that come into service after September 11, 2009.
2010	The EPA published revised national emissions standards for hazardous air pollutants, including mercury, from gold and silver production facilities. The standards reduce the maximum mercury emission level from 59 kilograms of mercury per 1 million metric tons of ore processed to 38 kilograms of mercury per 1 million metric tons of ore processed.
2011	The EPA finalized rules for performance standards and emission guidelines for sewage sludge incineration designed to reduce the amount of waste generated from dental offices.

In spite of limited production of mercury, the United States has a substantial amount of elemental mercury in Government and industry stocks. The National Defense Stockpile (NDS) held an inventory of 4,436 t of mercury at several sites in the United States in 2012. Mercury sales from the NDS were suspended in 1994 in response to environmental concerns. The U.S. Department of Energy (DOE) has stockpiled an additional 1,200 t of mercury in storage facilities in Oak Ridge, Tennessee (Virta, 2013). At yearend 2009, industry stocks of mercury from consumers and dealers in the United States are reported to be 30 t, but these stocks exclude material included as process inventory, in structures, or as site waste of the chloralkali manufacturing industry (Brooks, 2011).

Consumption and emissions of mercury in the United States have decreased as a direct result of increasingly stringent regulations that have limited use of mercury. The amounts of mercury produced from gold mining and mercury that is recycled in the United States also has changed slightly since 1970. The most recent U.S. legislation on mercury is the Mercury Export Ban Act of 2008 (MEBA), which prohibited Federal sales and the export of elemental mercury from the United States beginning on January 1, 2013. Increased amounts of surplus mercury were being exported in 2008 and 2009 in anticipation of the mercury export ban. Supply or stocks of mercury in the United States that had not been exported before 2013 and are not designated for short-term use in the United States must be stored under stringent conditions outlined by the MEBA.

PRIMARY PRODUCTION AND PROCESSES

Mercury has not been produced as a principal mineral commodity in the United States since 1992, but it has been recovered as a byproduct from processing of gold-and silver-ore at several mines in Nevada. Unlike small artisanal mining operations in developing countries, mercury is not used to extract gold or silver at mines in Nevada. The presence of mercury in ores from these mines is a result of the coincidence of mercury in certain gold ores, which is released during processing. Retorts are used to recover elemental mercury from mercury-containing precipitates and from calomel collected from pollution control devices installed on roasters. A small amount of byproduct mercury is generated from the mining of copper, lead, silver, and zinc, although no data are available on the quantity of mercury produced from these sources. Mercury concentrations vary substantially from mine to mine, ranging from less than 0.1 gram per metric ton (g/t) of ore to about 8 g/t of ore, but the mercury content of most commercial ores is less than 1 g/t of ore (Miller, 2007). The USGS reported byproduct mercury production data from gold mining operations until 1992 when the McDermitt Mine closed and mercury production information was withheld to avoid disclosing proprietary data from the sole remaining producer. The average annual amount of byproduct mercury production from 1990 to 1992 was 79 t (Matos and Brooks, 2005).

In 2000, the United States imported 103 t of elemental mercury, mainly from Australia and Germany (Matos and Brooks, 2005). In 2010, the United States imported 294 t of mercury, believed to have been derived primarily as a byproduct from precious metals mining operations in Chile and Peru (Brooks, 2011). It is likely that the 11 t of mercury that was imported in 2010 from Germany was in anticipation of a ban of exports of mercury from the European Union to be implemented in 2011.

A variety of methods are used to recover mercury from gold ore owing to variation in composition and concentration of gold found in the deposits. During pretreatment, roasting or autoclaving volatilize the mercury, making it available for capture by air pollution control devices (Miller, 2007). Roasting can recover about 95 percent of the mercury at a commercial grade of at least 99.9 percent purity (Nowak and Singer, 1995). A roaster processing 2 million metric tons of ore with a mercury content of 2 g/t can yield 3.2 to 3.6 t of elemental mercury (Miller, 2007). If a cyanide leaching process is used, then gold and mercury cyanide complexes are retained on the activated carbon; mercury may be stripped from the carbon and recovered using electrowinning or the Merrill Crow process, but mercury recovery from carbon is difficult and expensive and not all the mercury is recoverable. Mercury-bearing sludge from the electrolytic process and mercury-zinc precipitate from the Merrill Crow process is retorted both onsite and offsite to vaporize and remove the mercury from the gold and silver. Mercury vapor is condensed and the elemental mercury produced is then sold (van Zyl and Eurick, 2000; Miller, 2007).

Common mercury pollution control systems include quenching of off-gasses by water spraying, particulate removal systems, sulfur dioxide scrubbers, and carbon adsorption. Calomel can be recovered from waste treatment of metal mining. The Boliden-Norzink process can be used to remove mercury from flue gases to make calomel (U.S. Environmental Protection Agency, 2009).

Mercury in various forms is sold to U.S. recycling companies. Some gold processing operations process byproduct elemental mercury onsite and sell it through contracts to U.S. recycling companies, whereas others send calomel, mercury-bearing sludge, mercury-zinc precipitates, and (or) mercury collected on pollution control devices to recyclers for further processing. Because these byproducts are not considered waste, companies are not required to report production data to the Toxics Release Inventory database (U.S. Environmental Protection Agency, 2009, p. 19). Since 2006, however, the Nevada Mercury Control Program requires that companies that produce mercury compounds in Nevada must report annual mercury production and emission statistics to the Nevada Division of Environmental Protection. Data from 2006 to 2010 were used in preparing figure 2.

Figure 2 shows an estimate of the amount of mercury recovered from gold mining in Nevada from 2001 through 2011, based on the amount of ore processed annually at selected sites as reported by the company and historical mercury production figures from selected mines (Miller, 2007; Nevada Division of Environmental Protection, 2012). The estimates shown in figure 2 are in general agreement with other estimates of the amount of mercury produced from the region. Miller (2007) estimated Nevada byproduct mercury production in 2001 to be 97 t. Data reported by the Nevada Division of

Environmental Protection include mercury contained in calomel, sludge, and recovered elemental mercury. The leading source of mercury from Nevada gold mines is the Goldstrike Mine owned by Barrick Gold Corporation. In 2010, about 41 t of calomel and 13 t of elemental mercury were recovered from roasting and retorting operations at Goldstrike (Nevada Division of Environmental Protection, 2012). Available data of reported production and historical mercury production at selected mine sites allow for the calculation of estimates of about 90 t of contained mercury recovered in 2001 and 92 t of elemental mercury and mercury contained in compounds recovered in 2010 by gold companies and mercury recycling companies in the United States. For 2001 through 2011, an average of 96 t of contained mercury was recovered annually from Nevada gold mining operations, but that amount varies depending on mercury content of the ore. Production has decreased an average of 22 percent annually since 2000.

In 2006, the Nevada Division of Environmental Protection instituted the Nevada Mercury Control Program, which applies to all precious metal mining operations with thermal process units and requires the use of best available technology for maximum reduction in mercury emissions (Elges, 2011). In 2010, the EPA published revised national emissions standards for hazardous air pollutants, including mercury, from gold-and silver-production facilities. Mercury emission levels (Nevada Division of Environmental Protection, 2012) suggest that the availability of improved collection and suppression technology, increasing regulation, and technological improvements made by the industry have led to the decrease in mercury emissions from Nevada mines of about 95 percent from 2001 to 2011 that is shown in figure 2 (Elges, 2011).

Historically, elemental byproduct mercury (grading 99.9 percent pure) recovered from gold ore and calomel collected on pollution-control equipment used in Nevada gold mining has been sold or transferred to three mercury processing and recycling facilities in the United States—Bethlehem Apparatus Company, Inc., Hellertown, Pennsylvania; D.F. Goldsmith Chemical and Metal Corp. (subsidiary DFG Mercury Corp.), Evanston, Illinois; and WM Solutions, Union Grove, Wisconsin (Miller, 2007). The EPA monitors mercury emissions from each of these companies. These facilities also process or recycle mercury from other mercury-containing products and chemicals. For example, Bethlehem Apparatus uses equipment capable of recovering elemental mercury from calomel. Other leading U.S. recycling companies recover mercury from a variety of products include AERC Inc., Allentown, Pa.; Clean Harbors Environmental Services Inc., Braintree, Massachusetts; and Veolia Environmental Services Inc., Lombard, Ill.

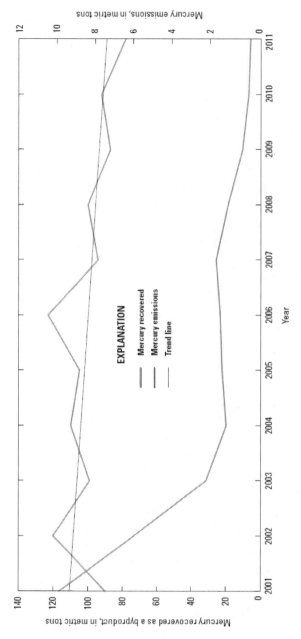

Figure 2. Mercury emissions and mercury recovered annually from Nevada gold mining operations from 2001 through 2011. The trend line shows an overall 22 percent decrease in mercury recovery from 2001 through 2011. The average annual amount of mercury recovered is estimated to be 96 metric tons. This average estimate is in general agreement with Miller (2007) and U.S. Environmental Protection Agency (2007) and was generated based on reported mine site production levels and historical mercury production statistics reported to the Nevada Division of Environmental Protection. Mercury emission levels are reported by the Nevada Division of Environmental Protection (2012).

SECONDARY SOURCES OF MERCURY

In the United States, less than 100 t of mercury was produced annually from 1996 through 2010 as a byproduct of gold and silver mining, primarily in Nevada (Nevada Division of Environmental Protection, 2012), so recycled mercury is the leading source of production of mercury in the United States. Recycled mercury is also recovered in the United States from mercury-containing products, such as batteries; compact and traditional fluorescent lamps; dental amalgam; electrical switches, relays, sensors; measuring instrumentation and thermostats; and medical devices. Although thermostats contain a switch, they have been classified with instruments and measuring devices to conform to the reporting format used by the USGS in the past. Mercury-containing scrap and industrial waste materials are imported into the United States through established contracts with U.S. recyclers for the recovery of elemental mercury.

The increase in mercury regulation has resulted in an overall reduction in the amount of mercury used in consumer products as well as an increase in mercury recycling, particularly in those jurisdictions where recycling of mercury in products is mandated. More than 60 companies recycle mercury-containing products in the United States (Association of Lighting and Mercury Recyclers, 2012). These recycling companies and State and local government recycling collection agencies separate out mercury waste for further processing at the six leading mercury recycling companies in the United States. Mercury recycling information is limited because companies are not required to report recycling statistics, many mercury wastes are reported generically as hazardous wastes, and there is no data collection or reporting program at the national level. Recycling data may be available from summaries of periodic recovery programs, selected State or municipal statistical reports, and data provided by individual recyclers.

Part of the difficulty in reporting national mercury recycling statistics is a result of the different product mixes and processes used by the major mercury recycling companies to recover mercury metal. The capacity of each facility to reprocess or recover mercury is different from that of other facilities, and each operation varies with the type and form of mercury product that is received. Mercury recovery technology is often different for different mercury-bearing products, and each company uses a combination of proprietary methods to extract mercury from their product waste stream.

In the United States, treatment and disposal of many mercury-containing wastes are managed under the Resource Conservation and Recovery Act

(RCRA), which requires that wastes or materials listed in the RCRA that fail the TCLP test be managed as hazardous waste. However, some wastes that contain mercury are not regulated as hazardous wastes under the RCRA (U.S. Government Accountability Office, 2005). Such materials include mine overburden and tailings, which can be landfilled; lamps and mercury-containing equipment, commonly treated as universal waste and managed separately before retort; and household waste, which can be landfilled or incinerated under the household exclusion to hazardous waste of the RCRA. Wastes can be exported to facilities outside the United States that meet standards equivalent to those in the RCRA (such as Canadian regulations allowing the stabilization and landfill of this material), and U.S. companies export mercury waste to Canada for treatment and disposal.

Thermal distillation and retort systems are most commonly used to recovery mercury, but separate retorts must be used for fluorescent lamps and other electrical or electronic devices and instrumentation. Depending on processing technology, mercury recovery rates can vary from 50 percent to more than 99.5 percent (Bethlehem Apparatus Company, Inc., 2012c). The amount of mercury metal that is treated, produced, landfilled, or sold to domestic or overseas markets by U.S. recyclers of mercury can vary from year to year owing to fluctuations in the price of mercury and changes in market demand. The global mercury recycling rate is estimated to be less than 10 percent (United Nations Environment Programme, 2011), and the U.S. mercury recycling rate for sectors where product recycling is taking place is less than 25 percent, except for the chloralkali manufacturing and the gold mining sectors. The mercury recycling rate attributed to chloralkali manufacturing has been estimated to be 50 percent (Maxson, 2006); the mercury recycling rate for the gold mining sector has not been reported.

In the past 4 to 5 years, the majority of mercury recycled by the major companies has been from imported mercury-containing materials and mercury from closed chloralkali plants. Because a large part of the source of mercury for large recyclers is derived from short-term supply contracts (the amount of material sent to a recycling facility fluctuates greatly from year to year from hundreds of tons of material to nothing, static (single-year) data reporting can be misleading (Bruce Lawrence, present, Bethlehem Apparatus Company, Inc., written commun., September 20, 2012).

AERC Incorporated reprocesses 21 to 30 t of mercury annually (Carpenter and others, 2011). Bethlehem Apparatus processes more than 900 t of mercury waste annually (Bethlehem Apparatus Company, Inc., 2012b). D.F. Goldsmith Chemical and Metal Corporation (DFG), which is not permitted to handle hazardous wastes, processes about 20 t of mercury annually from its distillation plant, but acts as a mercury broker by purchasing mercury from other recyclers for domestic or foreign resale. DFG also appears to be a buyer of mercury from closed chloralkali plants in the United States (Carpenter and others, 2011), but this could not be substantiated. WM Solutions Incorporated (formerly Mercury Waste Solutions) treats mercury waste containing an unknown mercury content from a variety of sources; the company processes more than 1,633 t of waste annually (Carpenter and others, 2011).

Because the amount of mercury in products such as lamps is nominal, the large recyclers have lost some business to small recyclers that specialize in lamp recycling. Overall, the U.S. lamp recycling rate is about 24 percent. In 2012, about 600 million lamps were available for recycling (Association of Lighting and Mercury Recyclers, 2012).

Available data suggest that the total amount of mercury recovered annually from recycled products in the United States is likely to range from 50 t to 265 t, depending on the level of supply of material from imports or closed chloralkali plants in a given year. Concorde reported that an estimated 115 t of mercury was recovered from products in the United States in 2006; this estimate did not include material from the chloralkali or gold mining industries (Maxson, 2006). Increased demand for mercury from artisanal gold producers and increased recycling of dental amalgam, fluorescent lights and CFLs, and mercury-containing thermostats has led to increased recycling in the United States. The DOE provided an average annual estimate of about 62.5 t from mercury waste and recycling operations in the final environmental impact statement for long-term management and storage of elemental mercury (U.S. Department of Energy, 2011, p. 3). This amount is likely to decrease once the mercury export ban is implemented in 2018 because the ban will likely reduce mercury imports to a level sufficient to meet U.S. demand, reducing the amount that is recycled in the United States because processed mercury could not be re-exported under the MEBA.

Discarded mercury-containing products, such as automobile convenience switches, batteries, chemicals, dental amalgam, electrical and electronic instrumentation, instruments and measuring devices, lighting, and thermostats, are the primary sources of old mercury scrap. Some of these products are collected locally or regionally but few nationwide programs exist for collecting mercury products. Most collected mercury-containing products are processed at a few major recycling companies. Bethlehem Apparatus, for example, processes more than 50 types of mercury-bearing chemicals, devices, and materials (Bethlehem Apparatus Company, Inc., 2012a). WM Solutions (a subsidiary of Waste Management, Inc.) processes batteries, computer boards, lamps, medical devices, and waste soil and water from chloralkali manufacturing, dental facilities, and gold mining.

USES OF MERCURY

In 1980, the three principal industrial uses of mercury were batteries (1,000 t), chloralkali manufacturing (330 t), and paint (300 t) (Matos and Brooks, 2005). By 1990, primarily as the result of regulation and technological advances, mercury use in batteries had decreased to about 100 t and paint use was about 20 t; the primary use of mercury was in chloralkali manufacturing (250 t) and instruments and measuring devices (110 t). By 2000, mercury was used only in small, button-cell batteries; manufacturers of most fungicides and paint were no longer using mercury, and annual use in chloralkali manufacturing had decreased by 76 percent from 1980 to 80 t. In 2001, mercury use in products (excluding chloralkali manufacturing) accounted for 245 t in wiring devices and switches (42 percent), instruments and measuring devices (28 percent), dental equipment and supplies (14 percent), and electrical lighting (9 percent), and other applications (7 percent) (U.S. Environmental Protection Agency, 2007). Figure 3 illustrates the amount of mercury used in the principal end-use categories for selected years from 1980 through 2010.

Over time, the distribution of mercury use has changed significantly as Federal and State regulations have limited some uses (such as paint and batteries), consumers (such as chloralkali manufacturers) have voluntarily reduced their use of mercury, and new technology has increased mercury use in lamps used in lighting. In 2007, consumption of mercury in the United States was estimated to be 67 t, primarily in switches and relays (42 percent), dental amalgam (22 percent), and lighting (14 percent) (Wienert, 2009). In 2010, estimated mercury recovery was about 52 t from recycling of products in the United States. Principal sources of mercury from recycled products in the United States included dental amalgam (estimated in this report to account for 57 percent of U.S. recycled product supply) and switches and relays (29 percent). In 2010, the chloralkali industry in the United States consumed less than 1 t of mercury. Additional sources of mercury supply in the United States in 2010 included imported mercury (294 t), byproduct mercury from gold mining (92 t), and mercury contained in imported products and scrap (38 t). The mercury that was produced from these sources and was not required to meet demand for mercury in the United States was processed, then exported. Mercury imports and exports from 2008 through 2010 were at a level higher than previous years in anticipation of the mercury export bans that were enacted in the European Union in 2011 and scheduled to be enacted in the in the United States in 2013.

Use of mercury in the chloralkali industry decreased as mercury-cell plants were closed or converted to nonmercury technologies. In 1996, there were 14 mercury-cell chloralkali plants in operation in the United States. By 2010, four plants were in operation, and by the end of 2012, only two plants were operating as mercury-cell chloralkali plants; one plant closed and one plant was converted to membrane technology, which does not use mercury. The passage of the MEBA in 2008 accelerated plans for closures of mercury-producing or mercury-refining plants in anticipation of the ban on mercury exports. As mercury-cell plants are decommissioned, much of the mercury recovered from processing equipment, structures, and waste is exported because the large volume (typically more than 200 t) of mercury recovered from these facilities is greater than U.S. demand for mercury (U.S. Environmental Protection Agency, 2009). As global regulations make it more difficult to import, sell, or dispose of mercury, industries using mercury must increasingly rely on recycled mercury for their needed supply or find acceptable substitutes for mercury for each end-use application (table 2). End-use markets are discussed individually in this report because of consumption, recyclability, and supply differences among the markets.

There are no Federal mandates for mercury recycling, except for large methylmercury batteries. Recycling mercury from other products varies from State to State depending on the extent to which the State promotes mercury recycling. Some States have well developed mercury recycling programs and others have none. Thus, available mercury collection data vary by State and product. In 2001, the Interstate Mercury Education and Reduction Clearinghouse (IMERC) was created to collect data on mercury reduction activities and programs offered by States. In 2007, the IMERC collected mercury recycling data from 15 member States. In 2011, six companies accounted for the majority of recycled mercury recovery in the United States. Mercury-containing automobile convenience switches, barometers, computers, dental amalgam, fluorescent lamps, medical devices, thermostats, and some mercury-containing toys were collected through State- and city-sponsored programs, industry-sponsored programs, or from individuals, sorted and processed by as many as 50 small companies, then shipped to the six large companies for retorting and reclamation of the mercury. Excess mercury processed and recovered by recyclers is sold on international markets (U.S. Environmental Protection Agency, 2009).

The largest nationwide recycling programs for which data are available are the National Vehicle Mercury Switch Recovery Program (NVMSRP), started in 2006 by the EPA to reduce mercury emissions when vehicles are scrapped and parts are reused or remanufactured, and the mercury-switch recycling program conducted by the Thermostat Recycling Corporation since 1997. Data collected by the NVMSRP are provided by vehicle manufacturers to End of Life Vehicle Solutions Corporation, an organization that maintains and promotes the environmental activities of the automotive industry. Available recycling data derived from these programs and other sources are reported in the following discussions.

Figure 4 summarizes the principal sources and distribution of the supply of primary and recycled mercury and quantifies the flow of mercury in the United States in 2000 and 2010. Much of the data in figure 4 is estimated, and the values and volumes of many categories of mercury-containing material described here and in the following discussions have changed significantly since 2000. It should be noted that data can change from year to year with variations in mercury collection activities, changes in the amount of mercury that is imported for processing, and closure of chloralkali plants, which can add to mercury supply and cause flow estimates to vary from average levels. Reliable annual data are difficult to obtain because the use of mercury has been in decline, mercury is a low-volume commodity, and tracking of mercury recycling and sales are not mandated.

Figure 4 shows data from Matos and Brooks (2005) and estimates generated for this report. Matos and Brooks (2005) reported data for 2000, and this report includes data for 2010; the two studies used similar methodologies. Figure 4 shows two added components (indicated by dashed lines) that were not reported separately by Matos and Brooks (2005). The amount of mercury contained in imported products and scrap was estimated to be 38 t, and the amount of mercury contained in industrial waste generated from gold mining and a mercury-cell chloralkali plant that was decommissioned in 2009 was estimated to be 111 t.

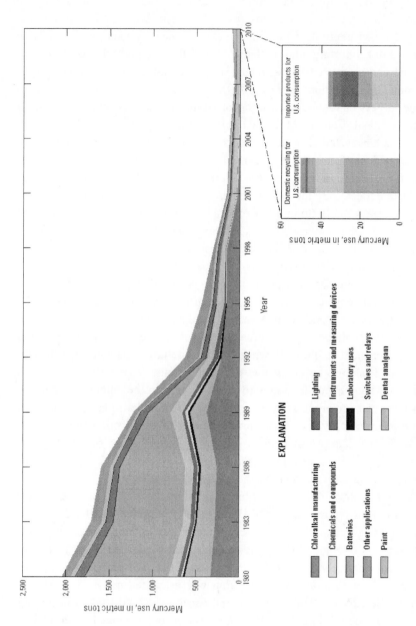

Figure 3. Principal end uses of mercury in the United States for selected years since 1980. Data for 1980 through 1998 are from Matos and Brooks (2005), for 2001 through 2007 are from Wienert (2009), and estimates for 2010 were generated for this report.

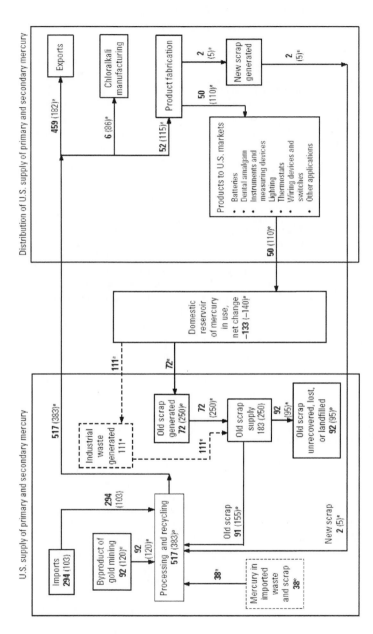

Figure 4. The flow of mercury in the United States in 2000 and 2010. Quantities are in metric tons of contained mercury. Values in bold reflect quantities in 2010; values in parenthesis reflect quantities in 2000 as reported by Matos and Brooks (2005). Industrial waste derived from soils from chloralkali plants that have been closed, industrial process waste, and waste imported from Canada were not reported in 2000. Values exclude dissipative losses. e, estimated.

Table 2. Principal end uses of mercury and possible mercury-free substitute

Product or application	Alternatives	Cost relative to mercury technology
Mercury cell process, used in chloralkali manufacturing	BAT is mercury-free membrane technology. Non- asbestos diaphram technology also considered BAT	Overall alternative technology costs are similar to higher than mercury-cell costs, primarily because conversion costs are significant; however membrane process costs for waste disposal, electricity, and raw materials are lower than for the mercury cell process.
Dental amalgam	Wide variety of potential alternative materials that include gold, silver, gallium, ceramic, porcelain, polymers, and composites are available, but not all are fully capable of substitution	Costs vary from less to more; some more easy to apply and others more difficult; none of the alternatives require specialized wastewater treatment required when using mercury amalgam.
Mercuric-oxide and mercury-zinc button cell batteries	Mercury-free zinc-air batteries and other alternatives containing less than 10 milligrams of mercury are available. Button cell batteries are still produced for selected applications	Battery cost can be higher, but collection and disposal of alternative battery types are not necessary, so these costs can be avoided.
Batteries of other types	Standard and rechargeable mercury- and cadmium-free batteries available	Standard mercury-free batteries cost about the same as those being replaced; purchase costs of cadmium-free rechargeable batteries are significantly higher, but costs become less expensive if battery is recharged more than 10 to 15 times.
Medical thermometers	Many alternatives, including single-use, electronic, and glass thermometers containing a gallium-indium-tin alloy	When first initiated, digital thermometers were more expensive; the cost of gallium-indium-tin thermometers should approach the cost of mercury thermometers over time as more are produced.
Other thermometers	Nonmedical thermometer alternatives to mercury include digital sensors (most common) or thermometers that	Large variation in price; long life of an electronic thermometer may make cost competitive with mercury

Product or application	Alternatives	Cost relative to mercury technology
	use gas or other liquids; choice depends on the temperature range, application, and need for precision (for a small number of precision applications, mercury thermometers are still preferred)	thermometer if price annualized
Laboratory equipment	Alternative technologies are available	Costs are generally similar.
Pesticides	Banned in many countries; principal alternatives include processes not requiring pesticides or easily degradable, narrow considerable; effectiveness of alternatives targeted with minimal environmental not documented. effect	It is likely that in most cases the costs are comparable, and environmental benefits are considerable; effectiveness of alternatives not documented.
Pressure measuring and control equipment	Alternatives include flexible membranes, piezoelectric crystals and other sensors, and fiberoptic pressure sensors; in U-tube meters, barometers, manometers, mercury can be replaced by another liquid or gas; for remote transmission of readings, a mercury transmitter containing up to 8 grams of mercury can be replaced with a potentiometer or a differential transformer that transmits an electronic signal (a diaphragm sensor is also commonly used)	Costs are generally similar.
Tilt-switch used in circuit control, thermostats, or communications	Manual, rolling ball, alternative fluid, microswitch	Costs are generally similar.
Electronic switch used in circuit control, thermostats, or communications	Solid-state switch, optical switch	Costs are generally similar.
Reed-switch	Solid-state switch, electrical-optical switch, semiconductor	Costs are generally similar.

Table 2. (Continued)

Product or application	Alternatives	Cost relative to mercury technology
Proximity sensor	Inductive sensor, capacitive sensor, photoelectric sensor	Costs are generally similar.
Energy-efficient (CFL) lamps	LED-based lamps	Costs are higher than traditional lamps.
Artisanal gold extraction	Possible alternatives include a nonmercury electrolytic process used in Brazil, but not widely accepted, or the Minataur process developed in South Africa	Costs are higher because only used on a small scale.

[Data are from United Nations Environment Programme (2002, p. 141–144). BAT, best available technology; CFL, compact fluorescent light; LED, light emitting diode]

Because the mercury recycling sector is undergoing considerable change, flows of mercury in the United States have changed considerably from year to year as the U.S. manufacturing industry adjusts to the export ban of mercury from the European Union enacted in 2011 and prepares for the export ban of mercury from the United States that is scheduled to take effect in 2013. It is likely that the data for 2010 may be considerably different from mercury flows in 2011 and 2012 as mercury use in chloralkali manufacturing diminishes, material from mercury-cell plants is recovered and exported, and existing mercury stockpiles are depleted in anticipation of the U.S. mercury export ban. A summary of the details in figure 4 follows.

Elemental mercury import data (294 t) and export data (459 t) are published by Brooks (2011). Data do not include mercury contained in imported or exported products, but may include material imported for processing then exported for foreign consumption.

Mine byproduct mercury data (92 t) were estimated based on company-reported mine site gold production levels and historical mercury production statistics as reported by Miller (2007) and the Nevada Division of Environmental Protection (2012). Data on the production of mercury as a byproduct from gold mining in the United States from 1988 through 2004 and in 2006 were compiled and compared with gold production data for the same years. Byproduct mercury production data for 2005 and 2011 were estimated based on the observed relationships between gold and mercury production from producing mines in years where mercury production was reported.

Estimates for 2006 through 2010 were developed based on company data reported to the Nevada Division of Environmental Protection. Data include mercury recovered from calomel (mercurous chloride, a mercury-bearing byproduct (about 85 percent mercury) formed during gold processing that is captured by pollution-control devices at smelters and retorted offsite to recovery mercury). About 517 t of mercury was recovered in 2010. Of the mercury processed in the United States, 57 percent was derived from imports, 25 percent came from old product scrap, 18 percent was recovered as a byproduct of gold mining, and less than 0.4 percent came from new scrap.

In 2000, about 115 t of mercury was used in the fabrication of various products, primarily switches and thermostats. Honeywell International, Inc., the largest producer of mercury-based thermostats and switches in the United States, stopped producing mercury-based products in the United States in 2006. In 2010, about 52 t of mercury was used in the fabrication of products. The 50 t shown as products to U.S. markets in the distribution section of figure 4 reflects the amount of mercury contained in products produced in the United States for domestic consumption or export. The estimated amount of mercury used in 2010 is lower than prior years because of the closure of mercury cells in the chloralkali manufacturing sector and declining use of mercury in other product sectors. Brooks (2011) reports mercury use to be "less than 100 t".

In 2010, about 38 t of mercury contained in imported products and scrap was estimated to have been processed and recycled in the United States. No data are available on the amount of such material processed in 2000.

The reservoir of mercury in use in the United States includes mercury contained in fabricated materials such as automobile convenience switches, dental amalgam, fluorescent lamps, and thermostats produced in prior years and still in use. It also contains mercury produced from domestic recycling, recovered from process equipment from recently decommissioned chloralkali plants for domestic use or export, recovered from contaminated soils, equipment, or structures associated with decommissioned chloralkali plants or gold processing, or recovered by recycling of imported waste products. Consequently, the reservoir of mercury in use can vary significantly from year to year.

The old scrap supply (183 t) for 2010 includes 72 t of postconsumer scrap generated by recycling of mercury-containing products in the mercury reservoir in the United States that were fabricated before or during the specified year. The old scrap supply also includes 111 t of mercury contained in industrial wastes from a chloralkali plant that closed in 2009, residues from dental facilities and the gold industry, and imported waste from Canada, materials that were not reported separately in the 2005 study. Although data on mercury from industrial sources is limited, the quantity that becomes available in any given year can vary significantly from year to year.

Estimates of the amount of old scrap generated from discontinued or discarded products has decreased from about 250 t in 2000 to about 72 t in 2010. Estimates of the amount of old scrap consumed (155 t in 2000 and 91 t in 2010) reflect the amount of mercury processed or recycled for export or reuse in the United States and derived from the recovery of industrial wastes and fabricated products.

Old scrap unrecovered, lost, or landfilled (95 t in 2000 and 92 t in 2010) is an estimate of the amount of mercury in discarded products containing mercury that is stored, lost during processing or incineration, discarded in landfills, discarded at dental facilities, or portions of dental amalgam lost during cremation or burial. It does not include dissipative losses to the air or water. In chloralkali manufacturing, mercury is purchased annually to replace mercury that is consumed during processing or lost to the environment. The Chlorine Institute reports that 6.5 t of replacement mercury was purchased in 2010 (Robyn Brooks, project engineer, The Chlorine Institute, Inc., written commun., August 8, 2012). Two mercury-cell chloralkali plants closed or were converted to nonmercury uses in 2012, leaving only two remaining plants in operation in the United States; the amount of mercury purchased for use in the remaining two chloralkali plants will likely be less than 1 t annually until these plants are decommissioned. New scrap (5 t in 2000 and 2 t in 2010) represents the amount of new mercury recovered in the United States during the product fabrication process and returned for recycling or reuse.

In 2000, 115 t of mercury was estimated to have been used in the United States in product fabrication; the corresponding consumption in 2010 was estimated to be 52 t based on data compiled by the USGS and supported by unpublished industry estimates (Bruce Lawrence, president, Bethlehem Apparatus Company, Inc., and Cynthia Manson, Industrial Economics, Inc., written commun., October 11, 2012). Specific amounts for each end use were not available. Estimates were derived from the total amount processed and recycled in the United States less the amount exported, used in the chloralkali industry, or placed in temporary storage for future use.

Chloralkali Manufacturing

The chloralkali industry was the leading consumer of mercury in the United States from 1988 to 2002 (Matos and Brooks, 2005). Since 1995, the amount of new mercury used by the chloralkali manufacturing industry in the United States has steadily declined by 98 percent from 136 t in 1996 to an estimated 0.3 t in 2010 because of increased efficiencies and closures or conversions to nonmercury technologies at mercury-cell plants; the industry continues to recycle mercury from its mercury-cell chloralkali plants. In 2005, the U.S. chloralkali industry reportedly recovered about 50 percent of the mercury waste generated in processing through onsite recycling; the balance was retained in processing equipment and soils until such time as the plant is decommissioned and additional mercury can be recovered (Maxson, 2006, p. 14).

The chloralkali manufacturing process is an electrolytic process that involves passing an electric current through a brine that contains either sodium chloride or potassium chloride to yield chlorine gas, a caustic solution of sodium hydroxide or potassium hydroxide, and hydrogen. Three types of electrolytic cells can host this reaction: the diaphragm cell, the membrane cell, and the mercury cell. Cells are differentiated in the way the chlorine is kept separate from the coproducts generated in the cathode. In the mercury cell, the mercury acts as a cathode and forms an amalgam with sodium that separates the sodium from the caustic and hydrogen production. Water is added to remove the sodium, and the majority of the mercury-bearing sludge is recycled onsite and reused in the electrolytic-cell process. Because mercury is recycled internally, this recycled mercury remains as part of the reservoir of mercury in use (Figure 4) and does not become available for part of the mercury flow as illustrated in figure 5 but becomes important when the plant is closed and the onsite mercury is sold. In 1992, the EPA banned disposal into the land of mercury-bearing sludge generated from the electrolytic production of chlorine-caustic soda (U.S. Bureau of Mines, 1993).

With the decline in the use of the mercury-cell, the diaphragm-cell, which involves an asbestos-based diaphragm (either asbestos or polymer-modified asbestos) that separates the cathodes from the anodes, has become the predominant chloralkali technology used in the United States. The membrane-cell technology is similar, but rather than using mercury or arsenic, it employs a plastic ion-exchange membrane to separate the anode and chlorine gas from the caustic product.

Increasing costs for energy associated with mercury-cell technology and increasing regulation of mercury and the industries that use it have resulted in increased costs for processing and maintenance of mercury-cell chloralkali plants, reducing the competitiveness of this technology on a global scale. As a result, chloralkali manufacturers have closed or are considering closing the mercury-cell plants or are converting mercury-cell plants to technologies that are less energy-intensive and mercury-free. In 1996, 14 mercury-cell plants with 762 cells were operating in the United States; by 2010, four plants with 244 cells were operating (The Chlorine Institute, Inc., 2009). Olin Corporation had two plants; the plant in Augusta, Georgia, closed in 2012, and the plant in Charles-ton, Tenn., was converted in 2012 to a membrane technology that does not require mercury (Olin Corporation, 2010). As of November 2012, the PPG Industries, Inc. 200-metric-ton-per- day mercury-cell production unit in New Martinsville, West Virginia continued to operate, and the company had applied for a variance to keep the plant in operation at least until January 2014 (PPG Industries, Inc., 2012). The Ashta Chemical plant in Ashtabula, Ohio, was expected to close by 2018 (Olin Corporation, 2010). In 2007, mercury-cell technology accounted for 10 percent of the total chloralkali capacity; in 2011, it was reported to account for 3 percent of chloralkali capacity (de Guzman, 2011).

Improvements in technology have reduced the mercury requirement for chloralkali production. In 1996, about 0.069 kilograms (kg) (0.153 pound) of mercury was required per metric ton of chlorine capacity; by 2008, only 0.005 kg (0.011 pound) of mercury was required per ton of capacity (The Chlorine Institute, Inc., 2009). Figure 5 shows estimates for the principal mercury flow steps as represented by the chloralkali manufacturing industry in 2008. The quantities of mercury flow in 2008 are significantly lower than correspond-ing estimates for 1996 (Sznopek and Goonan, 2000) because of plant closures and conversions and technological improvements driven by stringent regulatory limits on mercury emissions and disposal. In 1996, inventories in the chloralkali sector included 3,050 t of mercury, purchases were 136 t, and 27 t of mercury was landfilled or released into the environment. In 2008, however, inventories in the chloralkali sector had been reduced to 1,389 t of mercury, onsite recycling of mercury had supplemented much of the purchased mercury, and 3 t of mercury was released into the environment (The Chlorine Institute, Inc., 2009). In 2010, the chloralkali sector in the United

States purchased 6.5 t of mercury, used 0.3 t of mercury in chloralkali manufacturing, and released about 6 t of mercury to the environment (Robyn Brooks, project engineer, The Chlorine Institute, Inc., written commun., August 8, 2012).

From 1996 to 2010, six mercury-based chloralkali plants were closed, and four were converted (or scheduled to be converted) to membrane technology. Although many factors went into the decision whether to close or convert mercury-cell plants, the membrane process, which requires neither mercury nor asbestos, was chosen for all plants that were converted. In 2010, the chloralkali industry consumed 365 t of asbestos, or 35 percent of U.S. asbestos consumption, in 2010 (Virta, 2011).

A review of recent trends in the chloralkali industry can reveal how domestic and international regulation of the mercury industry can have unexpected global consequences. Increased regulation and voluntary plant closures have reduced mercury air and solid waste emissions from chloralkali manufacturing in the United States by about 85 percent from 2001 to 2008 (The Chlorine Institute, Inc., 2009); these changes to the structure of the industry have resulted in a significant amount of mercury released for sale on the international market from decommissioned mercury plants and from mercury recovered from recycled products. Although precise data on international trade are difficult to acquire, the United States has become a net exporter of mercury even though there has been no mining of mercury in the country since 1992. Regulations designed to reduce the amount of mercury available for global use can result in large, one-time releases of mercury into global markets with the recovery of mercury from decommissioned mercury-cell chloralkali plants. Implementation of the MEBA has accelerated this process.

Mercury (as elemental mercury and calomel) is recovered from stockpiles held by chloralkali manufacturers, electrolytic cells, and facility and soil decontamination efforts, but this material will no longer be available when all mercury-cell plants in the United States are decommissioned by 2018 and mercury contained in buildings and soils is recovered, sold, or stockpiled. A typical mercury cell contains an average of 4.7 t of process mercury (U.S. Environmental Protection Agency, 2010, p. 3–9). Thus, decommissioning 166 cells from the two plants expected to close in 2012 could yield about 780 t of mercury, not including onsite mercury stocks. The mercury content of contaminated buildings and soils could yield an additional 23 to 68 t of mercury per plant, depending on plant age, design, operating, maintenance, and waste disposal practices during the lifetime of the plant, and the amount of the mercury that could be recovered (Maxson, 2006). Mercury from closed plants is recycled by one of several large companies that recycle metals in the United States or is exported for recovery; data suggest that much of this mercury is sold through traders on the international market, and some of this mercury is ultimately purchased by numerous small-scale, unregulated artisanal gold mining operations in Africa, Asia, and Latin America. Stimulated by the increasing price of gold worldwide from 2005 to 2011, an increasing number of artisanal miners are producing gold using mercury, which is preferred by small miners rather than more complex processes than require materials such as cyanide. The production of gold using mercury is generally easier, faster, and cheaper and can produce a higher grade gold product than traditional panning methods (Lovitz, 2006).

Figure 6 compares exports of mercury from the United States from 1999 through 2011 with changes in mercury-cell chloralkali plant capacity, and table 3 lists the primary destinations of exports of mercury for years when large shipments of exported mercury took place relative to chloralkali plant closures. Large shipments to India, the Netherlands, Peru, and Vietnam seem to correlate with the closure of chloralkali plants in the preceding year. From 1999 through 2006, mercury was used for batteries, chlorine-caustic soda production, fungicides, lamps, and medical devices in India, and the country was one of the leading importers of mercury from the United States (Wankhade and Agarwal, 2003). Shipments to the Netherlands are also particularly notable; U.S. trade data show that, in total, 1,360 t of mercury was shipped to the Netherlands from 2006 through 2010, at a time when four chloralkali manufacturing plants were decommissioned. Shipments to the Netherlands accounted for 56 percent of total U.S. exports of elemental mercury in those 5 years. Simpson and Walsh (2012) suggest that much of this mercury is transported to warehouses of traders at the port of Rotterdam, and then is redistributed in smaller shipments to countries such as Colombia, where there is small-scale gold mining. India, Mexico, Peru, and Vietnam, countries that have also received large shipments of mercury from the United States, also have small-scale gold mining.

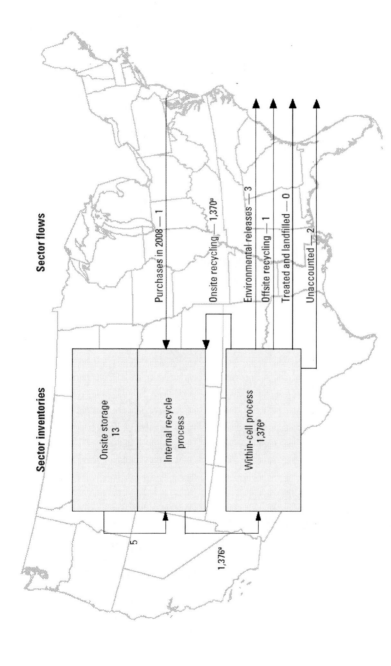

Figure 5. The flow of mercury from the mercury-cell process used in the chloralkali manufacturing industry in the United States in 2008. Data are derived from The Chlorine Institute, Inc. (2009) based on four plants in operation in 2008. Values are expressed in metric tons of mercury. e, estimated.

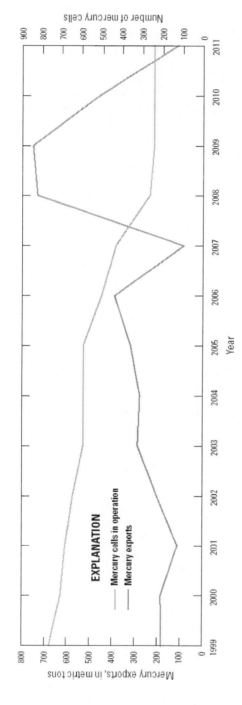

Figure 6. Relationship between mercury exports from the United States and the number of mercury cells in operation in the United States from 1999 through 2011. Export data from 1999 to 2010 are from U.S. Geological Survey (1997–2011). Data on mercury cells are from The Chlorine Institute, Inc., (2009). Estimated data for 2011 are derived from industry data and Brooks (2012).

**Table 3. Principal destinations of mercury exported from
the United States from 1999 through 2011**

Year	Principal destinations and quantity, in metric tons
1999	India, 85
2000	India, 65
2001	NA
2002	Netherlands, 73
2003	Netherlands, 57; Peru, 51
2004	Vietnam, 79; Mexico, 64; India, 63
2005	Netherlands, 156
2006	Netherlands, 118; India, 80; Vietnam, 74
2007	NA
2008	Netherlands, 535; Vietnam, 121
2009	Netherlands, 414; Peru, 110; Vietnam, 107
2010	Netherlands, 295
2011	Canada, 96

[Includes countries that received more than 50 metric tons (t) of mercury from the
United States. NA, no countries received more than 50 t]

In an international effort to reduce mercury sales for such use, a ban on mercury exports from the European Union took effect in 2011, and the MEBA would prohibit the sale and transfer of mercury outside the United States after January 2013. The MEBA would also place limits on the amount of mercury that could be imported if recyclers cannot export surplus mercury. Because chloralkali manufacturing plants have large amounts of mercury onsite, they have been affected by this legislation. Chloralkali plants in the United States that have not closed or been converted to nonmercury technology by 2013 would be required to store mercury at a site approved by the EPA for long-term mercury storage. Under the MEBA, the U.S. Department of Energy is required to designate one or more facilities for long-term management and storage of elemental mercury located within the United States. See the Effect of the Mercury Export Ban Act of 2008 on the U.S. Mercury Industry section for a further discussion.

Electrical and Electronic Instrumentation

Electrical and electronic applications accounted for 54 percent of the mercury used in the United States in 1980 (Matos and Brooks, 2005). Mercury use has subsequently decreased as a result of regulation, voluntary reduction in use, and the development of cost-effective non-mercury-containing alternative products.

Switches, Relays, and Sensors

Mercury has been used in electrical relays, sensors, and switches found in a variety of industrial and consumer products. Mercury switches include float switches, actuated by rising or falling liquid levels; tilt switches, actuated by a change in the switch position; pressure switches, actuated by a change in pressure; and temperature switches and flame sensors, actuated by a change in temperature. Mercury switches have been used in such devices as air conditioning equipment, appliances, automobiles and recreation vehicles, leveling devices, and security systems. Relays are devices that open or close electrical contacts. Mercury-containing relays have been used in cooking equipment and telecommunications circuit boards (Northeast Waste Management Officials' Association, 2008c, 2010d).

Some States and communities have placed restrictions on the sale and (or) distribution of mercury-containing switches and relays and have instituted reduction and collection programs for selected mercury-bearing products (Northeast Waste Management Officials' Association, 2010d). In response to these product bans and phase-outs, many companies have ceased manufacturing mercury switches and relays or stopped selling these devices in States that impose restrictions and in some cases curtailed sales nationwide. At least 11 States have ongoing collection programs for electrical or electronic products containing mercury; there are no ongoing nationwide collection programs for switches, except for switches used in vehicles as discussed in the Automobile Switches section.

Data collected by the IMERC for 2001, 2004, and 2007 provide an indication of the amount and industry trends of mercury use in sensors, switches, and relays. Mercury content varies with switch type, but most switches use about 1 gram (g) of mercury per switch. The data in table 4 show that the overall mercury content for switches, relays, and sensors decreased by 14 percent from 2001 to 2004 and a further 40 percent from 2004 to 2007, primarily as a result of mercury reduction efforts by manufacturers and States.

Automobile Switches

Mercury switches in automobiles accounted for about 50 percent of the mercury switches used in all applications in 2007. Mercury switches have been used in convenience lights and components of antilock brake systems (ABS) and ride control systems in many automobiles built from 1997 to 2006. In 2000, U.S. automakers used an estimated 4 million mercury switches each containing about 1 g of mercury (Brooks and Matos, 2006). Beginning in 1996, manufacturers of vehicles made outside the United States began phasing out mercury switches in new vehicles, and mercury switches were eliminated from vehicles manufactured in the United States after 2003. Even as mercury use in switches has decreased, new automotive applications of mercury, including high-intensity discharge (HID) headlamps and cold-cathode fluorescent lamps used in backlit instrument panels, entertainment systems, and navigation systems, are being introduced in some vehicles. A typical dashboard light bulb contains 0 to 5 milligrams (mg) of mercury; a tube-style bulb typically contains 5 to 10 mg, but may contain up to 100 mg of mercury. A convenience light switch and an ABS sensor contains about 1 g of mercury (Northeast Waste Management Officials' Association, 2008c). About 90 percent of the mercury in vehicles is contained in convenience lighting assemblies, and 9 percent is found in ABS switches or sensors (Corbett, 2005).

Table 4. Mercury use in switches, relays, and sensors

Product	Mercury content per unit, in grams	Applications	Total mercury content, in metric tons		
			2001	2004	2007
Tilt switches	0.05–5	Appliances, level controls, security alarms, thermostats	6.3	3.2	0.8
Float switches	0.1–67	Pumps	5.8	6.3	4.7
Flame sensors	>1	Stoves	2.3	1.1	0.9
Other switches	>1	Automobile convenience switches, antilock braking systems	19.1	18.9	12.8
Relays	0.005 – >1	Circuit boards, telecommunication systems	20.9	17.2	8.7
Total	NA		54.4	46.7	27.9

[Data are modified from Ashe and others (2012). NA, not applicable; >, more than]

In 2006, the NVMSRP was initiated as a cooperative effort by automobile manufacturers, the Environmental Council of States (ECOS), environmental organizations, the EPA, steelmakers, and vehicle dismantlers and shredders. Working with existing State mercury switch reduction and recycling efforts, the program set a goal to recover 80 to 90 percent of available mercury switches in the United States. Table 5 lists the results as of 2011. Between 2007 and 2011, the program had achieved an average estimated recovery rate of 21 percent. In 2011, the estimate for the amount of mercury in automotive switches in use in the United States was 31 t. An additional 2.7 t of mercury was contained in switches stockpiled or exported, and 0.7 t of mercury was recovered through recycling programs (End of Life Vehicle Solutions Corporation, 2012). These estimates exclude mercury contained in vehicles or vehicle components exported out of the United States.

Batteries

The use of mercury in consumer batteries has decreased significantly in the United States since the 1980s when battery manufacturing in the United States constituted the single leading use of mercury—1,000 t annually. By 1993, many battery manufacturers had begun selling mercury-free alkaline batteries, and the annual use of mercury in batteries by U.S. manufacturers decreased to about 10 t. Mercuric oxide button-cell batteries, containing 30 to 40 percent mercury by weight, were banned in the United States in 1996 under the Mercury Containing and Rechargeable Battery Management Act (MCRBMA). Mercuric oxide batteries larger than button-cell size are no longer available to the public but are still produced in limited quantities for military and medical applications where a stable current and longer service life is essential, as long as the manufacturer has established a procedure to collect, manage, and recycle end-of-life batteries. Button-cell batteries are still used in such applications as calculators, hearing aids, toys, and watches, but the MCRBMA limits the mercury content of button-cell batteries manufactured in the United States for these applications to 25 mg of mercury per button cell (National Electrical Manufacturers Association, 2002).

There are three different types of button-cell batteries that commonly contain mercury: alkaline manganese, silver-oxide, and zinc-air. Most alkaline manganese batteries are used in cameras, but they may be found in a variety of other devices. Silver-oxide button-cell batteries are used in calculators, cameras, games, medical devices, toys, and watches. Zinc-air button-cell batteries are used in hearing aids. In each of these types, a mercury coating is added to the cell to prevent the formation of hydrogen gas that can result in battery leakage and malfunction. Alkaline button-cell batteries produced in 2002 were estimated to have an average mercury content of 10.8 mg of mercury; silver-oxide button-cell batteries, 2.5 mg; and zinc-air button-cell batteries, 8.5 mg (Maine Department of Environmental Protection, 2005, p. 3). Since 2001, many States have enacted legislation restricting the sale of mercury button-cell batteries and (or) products that contain these batteries. U.S. battery manufacturers voluntarily committed to eliminate mercury in button-cell batteries by June 30, 2011, coinciding with the effective date of legislation in Connecticut, Maine, and Rhode Island that banned mercury-containing button-cell batteries in these States as of July 1, 2011 (Poon, 2011). The ban was extended for another 6 months because the supply of mercury-free button-cell batteries was disrupted as a result of the nuclear disaster in Fukushima, Japan, following the March 11, 2011, earthquake and tsunami (Fashion Jewelry and Accessories Trade Association, The, 2012).

Table 5. Mercury use in automotive switches

Year	Mercury in switches in use, in metric tons	Mercury in scrapped switches, in metric tons	Mercury in recovered switches, in metric tons	Mercury stockpiled, exported, or land-filled, in metric tons
1997	99	NA	NA	NA
1998	93	6	0	6
1999	87	6	0	6
2000	81	7	0	7
2001	74	7	0	7
2002	69	5	0	5
2003	63	5	0	5
2004	59	4	0	4
2005	54	4	0	4
2006	50	5	0.2	5
2007	45	5	0.7	4
2008	41	4	1	3
2009	38	4	0.9	3
2010	34	4	0.6	3
2011	31	3	0.7	3

[Data are from End of Life Vehicle Solutions Corporation (2012). NA, not available]

Data on mercury-added button-cell production and use in the United States are not readily available. Reports by the IMERC estimate that all mercury batteries sold in the United States for 2001, 2004, and 2007 contained about 2.5 t, 2.2 t, and 1.9 t of mercury, respectively; these data generally reflect replacement batteries only and do not include batteries imported to the United States or batteries contained in imported products. (Northeast Waste Management Officials' Association, 2010a). The decreasing trend shown by these data appears to fit the industry pledge to reduce mercury use in batteries by 2011. Data compiled by the IMERC show that mercury contained in products sold in the United States accounted for more than 0.9 t in 2001, 1.3 t in 2004, and 0.9 t in 2007, but not all manufacturers of products containing mercury-added batteries disclosed their U.S. sales to the IMERC (James, 2009). Another estimate of the total mercury contained in button-cell batteries sold in the United States in 2007 suggested a range of 3.3 to 4.6 t of mercury (James, 2009, p. 4).

Import and export data reported by the U.S. International Trade Commission suggest that the United States imported many more manganese dioxide, silver oxide, and zinc-air button-cell batteries that it exported. In 2010, manganese oxide batteries were imported to the United States primarily from China (60 percent), Indonesia (19 percent), and Germany (9 percent); silver oxide batteries were imported primarily from Japan (55 percent), Switzerland (26 percent), and Germany (14 percent); and zinc-air batteries were imported primarily from Germany (44 percent), the United Kingdom (29 percent), and China (12 percent) (U.S. International Trade Commission, 2012). These statistics likely include mercury-containing and mercury-free batteries, and it is difficult to separate these two types, although a rough approximation can be made by assuming that 10 percent of the batteries from China are mercury-free (Zero Mercury Working Group, 2012) and 39 percent of the batteries from the European Union are mercury-free (Mudgal and others, 2012, p. 126). Batteries from Indonesia were assumed to be similar in distribution to batteries from the European Union, and batteries from Japan are totally mercury-free (United Nations Environment Programme, 2007). Based on these assumptions, the net imports of mercury-containing button-cell batteries of all types to the United States contained an estimated 7.6 t of mercury in 2010. This value does not include the amount of mercury included in batteries contained in imported products.

Recycling of mercuric oxide batteries in the United States in 2010 is believed to be limited to the recovery of mercury from the large batteries discarded by medical institutions and the military. Recycling of this material is required by the MCRBMA and is part of the material processed by the leading U.S. recyclers, such as Bethlehem Apparatus. Specific data on the amount of this material recycle are not reported.

There are no Federal restrictions on the disposal of button-cell batteries in the United States, nor are there State-sponsored programs to collect the batteries (Maine Department of Environmental Protection, 2005). Recycling of button-cell batteries is limited to local battery collection programs. A nationwide button-cell battery collection program has not been implemented because collection of button cells is not thought to be cost-effective, primarily because of the small amount of mercury in each button-cell battery and the need to keep button-cell batteries separate from other batteries being recycled because of potential mercury contamination. The estimated costs and potential safety hazards of collection, transportation, and recycling were found to outweigh the benefits gained by recycling (National Electrical Manufacturers Association, 2003). Silver-oxide button-cell batteries are often collected by jewelers and large retailers when they replace watch batteries and recycle them to recover the silver. In cases where mercury-containing button-cell batteries are recycled, they are collected and sent to the leading U.S. recycling companies for processing.

Lighting

Although mercury continues to be an essential component in the commercial and residential lighting industry, the contribution of mercury to lamps continues to decrease even as the energy efficiency of mercury-containing lamps increases. Because a small amount of mercury is contained in fluorescent lamps and high-intensity discharge lamps, concerns over possible mercury releases to the environment have led the industry to develop products using less mercury and government entities to implement stricter regulation related to mercury emissions, use, and disposal. The USGS conducted a study of mercury flow in the U.S. mercury-containing lamp sector as of 2001 (Goonan, 2006). Since that time, Federal and State regulations have become increasingly complex, new products have been introduced into the market, and a greater emphasis has been placed on improving mercury recycling rates and developing mercury-free alternatives. A review of mercury use and recycling activities as of 2010 follows. Annual mercury use in the U.S. lighting sector was estimated to be about 17 t (Gheysens, 2011), 70 percent greater than the 2007 value of about 10 t of mercury sold for lighting as reported by the IMERC (Northeast Waste Management Officials' Association, 2008b; Wienert, 2009).

A typical fluorescent lamp is made up of a phosphor-coated glass tube with electrodes located at either end. When voltage is applied, the electrodes energize the mercury vapor and cause it to emit ultraviolet energy. A phosphor coating absorbs the ultraviolet energy, which causes the phosphor to fluoresce and emit visible light. Mercury-containing lamps require three to four times less energy and have a longer life than traditional incandescent bulbs (National Electrical Manufacturers Association, 2005).

Since 1990, legislation has been enacted and several regulations have been promulgated that indirectly affect mercury use in fluorescent lamps. The Energy Policy and Conservation Act of 1992 set energy conservation standards for certain classes of general service fluorescent lamps (GSFLs) and established provisions for periodic review of these standards. In 2008, the DOE completed the first review of the standards and determined that the standards needed to be updated; amended standards were published on July 14, 2009 (U.S. Department of Energy, 2009). Fluorescent lamps of a standard 4-foot length are generally classified based on their diameter expressed in eights of an inch, thus a T12 lamp would have a diameter of 12/8 (1.5 inches) whereas a T8 lamp would have a diameter of 8/8 (1 inch) (Merritt, 2012). Based on an analysis by the DOE, most T12 fluorescent lamps are considered too inefficient to meet the new standards and can no longer be manufactured after July 14, 2012; fluorescent lamps not meeting the new standards must be replaced by that date. T12 lamps contain more mercury than the T5 and T8 lamps that are replacing them. The Energy Independence and Security Act of 2007 included provisions for phasing out mercury-free incandescent light bulbs in favor of more energy-efficient compact fluorescent light (CFL) bulbs, which contain an average of 4 mg of mercury (U.S. Environmental Protection Agency, 2012f). Regulations promulgated since 1990 to increase the energy efficiency of commercial and residential lighting have contributed to an average reduction of mercury use in general service fluorescent lamps by 77 percent since 1985, but have increased mercury use in general service fluorescent lamps by 6 t through encouraging the use of mercury-bearing CFLs as a replacement for incandescent light bulbs.

Mercury content in GSFLs has decreased from an average of 48.2 mg of mercury in 1985 to as low as 3.5 mg of mercury for a standard T8 48-inch-long fluorescent lamp (Northeast Waste Management Officials' Association,

2008c). Several U.S. manufacturers produce a low-mercury fluorescent lamp, containing 3.5 to 4 mg of mercury compared with 8 to 14 mg of mercury contained in a standard (T12) fluorescent lamp (U.S. Environmental Protection Agency, 2012a).

Estimates of mercury use in the lighting sector for 2010 are listed in table 6. The U.S. lighting industry had an inventory of 45.6 t of mercury in 2001 from 4.2 billion lamps that were in use (Goonan, 2006). In 2010, the estimated mercury inventory was 28.8 t from about 4 billion lamps in use, a 37 percent decrease on mercury inventory from 2001. Various types of linear fluorescent lamps are reported separately to show that the highest proportion of the mercury in use is derived from the T12 lamps that are being phased out compared with the T8 and T5 lamps that are replacing them. Mercury use from the lighting sector will continue to decrease as fewer T12 lamps are produced. CFL lamps, which contain up to 4 mg of mercury, were developed as a replacement for incandescent lamps. The use of CFL lamps is expected to be of relatively short duration. Light-emitting diode (LED) lamps, which contain no mercury, are expected to eventually replace CFL lamps in many applications (Wilburn, 2012).

Total mercury emissions in the United States are expected to decrease partially owing to the amended lighting standards that took effect in 2012 (U.S. Department of Energy, 2012). The use of energy-efficient lighting reduces the amount of fuel used in powerplants, the primary source of airborne mercury emissions in the United States. Full implementation of energy-efficient lighting programs nationwide was estimated to result in a reduction of close to 10 t per year of mercury primarily owing to reduced coal-generated electricity (U.S. Environmental Protection Agency, 2006, p. 45). Mercury emissions in 2001 were estimated to be about 2.9 t from the lamp sector (Goonan, 2006). Based on a reduced inventory of mercury available from the lighting sector in 2010 and available recycling estimates, a rough estimate of the mercury emission level in 2010 would be about 2 t from lamp disposal, recycling, and transport operations, using the methodology developed by Goonan (2006). Much of the mercury that is released into the air occurs in the period after the lamp is broken, most often during transport to disposal or recycling facilities. The estimate may be overstated because it does not take into account the mercury control methods implemented since 2001 to reduce mercury emissions at incinerators, landfills, or recycling facilities.

Table 6. Mercury-containing lamps used in 2010

Lamp type	Lighting service use sector									
	Commercial		Industrial		Outdoor		Residential		Total	
	Lamps, in million units	Mercury content, in metric tons	Lamps, in million units	Mercury content, in metric tons	Lamps, in million units	Mercury content, in metric tons	Lamps, in million units	Mercury content, in metric tons	Lamps, in million units	Mercury content, in metric tons
CFL	216	0.7	0.4	0.001	12	0.048	1,322	5.3	1,550	6
T5 fluorescent	108	0.25	9.2	0.021	NA	NA	3.6	0.008	121	0.3
T8 fluorescent	996	4.5	83	0.4	NA	NA	70	0.3	1,149	5.2
T12 fluorescent	538	5.4	36	0.4	NA	NA	368	3.6	942	9.4
HID[1]	35	1.5	14	0.6	93	3.3	1.4	0.05	143	5.5
Miscellaneous	13	0.2	0.5	0.006	29	0.4	132	1.8	175	2.4
Total	1,906	12.6	143	1.4	134	3.7	1,897	11.1	4,080	28.8

Includes high-pressure sodium, low-pressure sodium, metal halide, and mercury vapor lamps. Adapted from U.S. Department of Energy (2012a).

[CFL, compact fluorescent light; HID, high-intensity discharge; NA, not available]

Most mercury-containing lamps fail to pass the toxicity characteristic leaching procedure (TCLP) test mandated by the RCRA and thus must be treated as a hazardous waste. In 1999, the EPA enacted regulations that allow lamps to be regulated under the universal waste rule of modified hazardous waste regulations developed for other widely generated wastes such as batteries. Almost all States have adopted this EPA rule without amendment, and many have developed lamp handling guidelines and (or) recycling programs or procedures. In spite of these actions, nationwide data on recycling rates are not well known as most States do not require reporting by generators or recyclers for universal wastes. For 2003, a nationwide recycling rate estimate of 23.3 percent for fluorescent lamps was reported (Association of Lighting and Mercury Recyclers, 2004). According to this estimate, the commercial recycling rate was 29 percent, and the residential recycling rate was 2 percent (Association of Lighting and Mercury Recyclers, 2004). The low recycling rate can be attributed to the low value of recycled materials found in lamps, which reduces the economic incentive for lamp recycling, which is estimated to cost $0.50 to $2.00 per unit (National Electrical Manufacturers Association, 2008), and the lack of coordinated collection programs. The growing market penetration of CFLs has led to a number of CFL collection programs, but recycling remains expensive relative to the price of the lamp. It is likely that government-mandated replacement of T12 lamps with more energy efficient T8 or T5 lamps at government facilities and large corporate replacement programs could result in a temporary increase in the recycling rate of fluorescent bulbs, but the overall effect of such activities is not reported.

There are no comprehensive data on the number of lamps that have been recycled. A number of States and municipalities have set up programs to recycle CFLs but few programs exist for recycling linear fluorescent tubes (Northeast Waste Management Officials' Association, 2009). Some States and municipalities offer bulb recycling programs on a regular or occasional basis, and others mandate CFL lamp recycling. In many areas nationwide, CFL recycling programs are being offered by manufacturers, retailers, or utilities. Nationwide home improvement chain stores, for example, offer CFL recycling programs. Most of the material collected by these selective recycling programs is sent for processing to one of the six large recycling companies. Aggregated annual recycling data are not reported.

Replacement of T12 lamps by T8 lamps or substitution of incandescent bulbs by CFLs yields a small change in material requirements. Replacing 250 million incandescent bulbs with CFLs would require about 1 t of mercury. As

LED technology displaces CFL technology in the lighting sector, less mercury would be required for the lighting sector. Production of large quantities of LEDs could potentially result in a more significant shift in the use of some metals or materials because LEDs require various metals such as arsenic, gallium, indium, and rare earth elements (Wilburn, 2012).

Instruments and Measuring Devices

Mercury has historically been used in a wide variety of instruments and measuring devices, which accounted for 8 percent of the mercury used in the United States in 1980. Such devices have been used in industrial and medical sectors because of the responsiveness of mercury to pressure and temperature. Minnesota was the first State to enact legislation in 1994 prohibiting the disposal of thermostats and other mercury-containing devices until the mercury had been removed. One outcome of this legislation was that Honeywell International, Inc., the leading manufacturer of thermostats in the United States at the time, started a thermostat recycling program in Minnesota. Since 2001, 13 States have enacted legislation banning the sale and use of mercury-containing measuring devices and thermometers (Northeast Waste Management Officials' Association, 2010c). In 2002, the EPA banned the sale of mercury-containing thermometers, and in 2010, issued a new rule under the Toxic Substances Control Act requiring that the EPA be notified at least 90 days before the beginning of production of mercury-containing devices (such as flow meters, natural gas manometers, and pyrometers) that come into service after September 11, 2009.

Measuring Devices

Mercury has been used in devices that measure liquid or gas flow (flow meters or strain gages), humidity (hygrometers or psychrometers), pressure (barometers, manometers, or sphygmomanometers), specific gravity (hydrometers), and temperature (pyrometers or thermometers). In 1990, about 110 t of mercury was used in the manufacture of such devices. In 1995, mercury content in such devices had decreased to 43 t; by 2000, mercury use in these devices had decreased to 30 t (Matos and Brooks, 2005). By 2001, environmental concerns related to mercury and Federal and State regulation had further reduced mercury use in these devices to 4.5 t (North-east Waste Management Officials' Association, 2010c). In 2007, the latest date for which data are available, mercury use had decreased to about 1 t (Wienert, 2009). It is reasonable to assume that most of these devices are no longer manufactured or sold in the United States, except in cases where there is a specialty application and no suitable, cost-effective substitute for mercury is available.

Devices that are no longer sold in the United States are considered legacy products, which may still be used, resold as a used product, or stored before disposal occurs. As with other mercury-containing devices, recycling is done on a State-by-State or local basis. Recycled material is most often collected and sent to one of the six major U.S. recyclers.

Mercury-free alternatives to many of these devices have become available. Depending on the device, these alternatives may include a device that uses a substitute liquid that has appropriate characteristics and is readily available (such as alcohol in a fever thermometer or manometer), an aneroid (liquid-free) device, or a digital device that performs a similar function. Increasingly, digital devices are used in many applications. However, many of these digital devices require a battery, some of which contain mercury. A mercury-containing button-cell battery may be used, particularly if the device is produced in China and imported to the United States. If such a battery is used, then the end-of-life device must be treated under the EPA universal waste rules.

For selected applications, measuring devices used in laboratories use mercury-based instrumentation because accurate alternatives with the appropriate characteristics may not yet be available. Although a variety of analog and digital thermometers have become available for use, they may not meet the requirements of a laboratory device that requires very precise measurement. The National Institute of Standards and Technology (NIST) is participating in several efforts to identify alternative thermometers for a broad range of measurement applications and coordinate efforts to replace mercury-containing laboratory devices (National Institute of Standards and Technology, 2012).

Thermostats

For many years, mercury has been used in thermostats, both as stand-alone units in businesses and residences and as a component in heating and cooling equipment. Thermostats have historically contained mercury switches to automatically maintain building temperatures at a set level by triggering furnace or air conditioner operation when the desired temperature is reached. Mercury content for a single mercury-switch thermostat can range from 2.7 to 10.8 g of mercury, with an average content of about 4 g of mercury (James, 2005). During the past 15 years, the annual demand for mercury in thermostat manufacturing in the United States has been reduced from 13 to 18 t (15–20 tons) in 1995 to 0.9 t (less than 1 ton) in 2010 (Mercury Policy Project, 2010). This reduction can be attributed to States regulating sales of new mercury thermostats and the subsequent cessation of mercury thermostat production by the top U.S. manufacturers. In 2005, about 83 percent of all thermostats contained mercury (New England Zero Mercury Campaign, 2005). Electromechanical and electronic thermo-stats have been developed to replace mercury-switch thermo-stats, although mercury-containing thermostats are still being manufactured in other countries. The composition of these devices varies depending on type; evaluation of material substitution for these devices is beyond the scope of this report.

Data collected by the IMERC for 2001, 2004, and 2007 provide an indication of the amount of mercury used in this sector and the prevailing industry trend. In 2001, about 13.5 t of mercury was contained in thermostats sold in the United States. In 2004, about 13.1 t or mercury was contained in thermostats sold. Between 2001 and 2007, 17 States instituted restrictions on the sale of mercury-containing thermostats, and a number of companies have voluntarily phased out products using mercury-switch thermostats or switched to electromechanical or electronic thermostats that do not contain mercury.

The IMERC reported that 3.5 t of mercury was contained in thermostats sold in 2007, a decrease of 73 percent from the amount found in thermostats in 2004 (Wienert, 2009; North-east Waste Management Officials' Association, 2010e).

The Thermostat Recycling Corporation (TRC) was established in 1997 by the three leading U.S. thermostat manufacturers to collect and recycle mercury-switch thermo-stats removed from service. In 2004, the EPA estimated that mercury thermostats found in homes and businesses contained a reservoir of about 200 t of mercury in thermostats (James, 2005) and that about 2.5 million mercury-switch thermostats containing 9 to 14 t (10 to 15 tons) are removed from service each year in the United States (Mercury Policy Project, 2010). At 4 g of mercury per thermostat, the amount of mercury that could potentially become available annually is 10 t.

A study conducted for the State of California estimated that 237,000 to 490,000 mercury-switch thermostats would be removed from service in 2010 in California based on the average maximum assumed thermostat age of 30 years (Thermostat Recycling Corporation, 2012b). Using population estimates for California and the Nation as a guide, the California estimates could be extrapolated to the United States as a whole, yielding an estimate of 2 to 4 million mercury-switch thermostats containing 8 to 16 t of mercury that potentially could have been removed from use since 2008. This estimate seems reasonable given that there has been no new production of mercury switches and many thermostats have since been replaced with nonmercury types.

The number of thermostats recycled by TRC is low when compared with estimates of the number of thermostats removed from service annually (Thermostat Recycling Corporation, 2012a). From 1999 through 2008, TRC recovered 3.3 t of mercury. For that same period, an estimated 80 to 160 t of mercury was contained in thermostats that were removed from service. Thus, TRC has collected less than 5 percent of the thermostats that were removed from service during that decade (Mercury Policy Project, 2010). Recycling rates vary from State to State, ranging from 1.3 percent in New York to 12.7 percent in Maine. States without established procedures for thermostat recovery may not recycle any mercury thermostats, although TRC reportedly has collection sites in 48 States. As of May 2012, TRC has recovered more than 1.4 million thermostats containing 6 t (6.6 tons) of mercury since it began mercury recycling in 1999 (Thermostat Recycling Corporation, 2012a).

If the TRC data are accurate and account for all domestic recycling of thermostats, then there is a significant amount of mercury contained in thermostats in use and more in thermo-stats that have been stored or discarded. Assuming 8 to 16 t of mercury contained in thermostats is removed from service annually, and assuming a 5 percent recycling rate, then 7.6 to 15 t of mercury may be stored or discarded each year. Although mercury contained in thermostats is less likely to be released to the air than mercury in fluorescent tubes, it may be released into the air or groundwater over time, thus making a significant contribution to U.S. mercury emissions.

Dental Amalgam

Dental amalgam containing about 50 percent mercury has been used for more than 150 years in the United States for restoration of posterior teeth in children and adults. In 1980, 80 percent of all restorations used amalgam. Historically, dentists mixed amalgam onsite, using bulk liquid mercury and metal powders; in 2011, most dentists purchased amalgam imported in predosed capsules with a mercury content varying from 100 to 1,000 mg (Northeast Waste Management Officials' Association, 2010b). Dental amalgam is considered a medical device that is regulated by the U.S. Food and Drug Administration (FDA). In 2008, the FDA reviewed the best available evidence to determine whether the mercury vapor emitted by mercury amalgam fillings was a cause of concern. Based on the findings, the FDA issued a final regulation on dental amalgam in 2009 that classified dental amalgam as a class II or moderate risk to society, allowing the agency to apply controls on product labeling and disposal. This designation also applies to other alternative restorative materials, such as composites or gold (U.S. Food and Drug Administration, 2009, 2011).

Since 2003, 11 States have mandated requirements for best management practices for dental amalgam waste so that dental offices capture and recycle this waste. Requirements include installing amalgam separators, properly managing solid waste that contains amalgam, and recycling amalgam. In States where amalgam use is not regulated, use of amalgam separators and amalgam recycling rates are low. Use of these practices can eliminate 95 to 99 percent of dental mercury from entering municipal wastewater (Reindl, 2010).

Dental amalgam in teeth represents the leading source of mercury in use in the United States. There may be an inventory of up to 290 t of mercury residing in the teeth of U.S. residents (Concorde East/West Sprl, 2012). The number of new or replacement amalgam fillings in the United States appears to have been decreasing by 3.5 to 4 percent per year (Beazoglou and others, 2007). A single-surface amalgam filling requires about 400 mg of mercury; a filling with three or more surfaces can use about 800 mg of mercury (Concorde East/West Sprl, 2012, p. 8). In terms of the amount of mercury used in dental amalgam, dental mercury use decreased on average by about 2 percent annually from about 61 t in 1980 to about 30 t in 2000 (Matos and Brooks, 2005). Data collected by the IMERC suggest that this trend continued from 2001 through 2007 when the amount of mercury sold from five U.S. producers of dental amalgam decreased from about 28 t in 2001 to about 15 t of mercury in 2007 (Northeast Waste Management Officials' Association, 2010b). Although the general trend of mercury use in dental applications is decreasing, the IMERC mercury-added products database for 2010 reports statistics for four companies that suggest that about 18 t of mercury was sold in the United States for dental applications in 2010 (Northeast Waste Management Officials' Association, 2012).

With increasing awareness of the potential health hazards associated with mercury, improvements in quality of substitute materials in some applications, and a decrease in the incidence of dental decay, use of dental amalgam is decreasing (U.S. Environmental Protection Agency, 2012c). Mercury-free alternatives to dental amalgam include resin composites, resin and glass ionomers (a polymer containing an ion made of glass or resin and an organic acid), porcelain, or gold alloys. Although the cost of these alternative materials has decreased, the typical cost to the consumer selecting an alternative filling material is higher than the cost of using amalgam. A recent study suggests the basic cost for an amalgam filling is $144 compared with $185 for a composite filling (Concorde East/ West Sprl, 2012, p. 2). These costs, however, do not include the costs associated with mercury collection, recycling, or mitigation of release of mercury emissions. In addition to cost, each type of restorative filling has certain advantages and disadvantages that must be evaluated by the consumer.

A study conducted by Concorde East/West Sprl (Concorde) suggests that he U.S. dental sector used about 30 t of mercury in 2009 (Concorde East/West Sprl, 2012, p. 21), a value considerably higher than that reported by the data collected by the IMERC. The NEWMOA recognizes that the data collected by the IMERC may underestimate the total amount of mercury sold in the United States because it does not include all sources of imported or exported material in its estimates (Northeast Waste Management Officials' Association, 2010b). The actual amount of mercury contained in dental amalgam used in the United States in 2010 likely is between the estimate of 18 t by the IMERC and the estimate of 30 t by Concorde (Adam Wienert, IMERC coordinator, Northeast Waste Management Officials' Association, oral commun., November 13, 2012). Assuming that domestic use in 2009 was similar to that in 2010, the available data suggest that as much as 12 t of mercury amalgam may have been imported to the United States to supplement the decreasing amount sold by domestic manufacturers. Figure 7 shows the mercury flow pattern for the dental sector in 2009 as developed by Concorde East/West Sprl. Mercury emissions data shown in figure 7 were developed based on data reported by Cain and others (2007).

Sources of mercury found in a dental office include new mercury amalgam purchased in predosed capsules, mercury amalgam removed from existing fillings, and mercury amalgam stocks in the dental office carried over from previous years. An additional source of mercury is amalgam recovered from lost teeth or teeth removed from deceased persons prior to burial or cremation.

The amount of mercury releases from dental amalgam to air, soil, and water as well as the effects of such releases on the environment and human health are being investigated by Government agencies and industry nongovernmental organizations. Of the 30 t of new mercury in dental amalgam reported to have been purchased by U.S. dental clinics in 2009 (Concorde East/West Sprl, 2012), 33 percent was discarded because it was not used during the procedure or it was removed from the tooth during the fitting of the filling (Figure 7). This relatively high discard rate can be attributed to the increasing use of purchased, prepackaged amalgam ampoules; a filling may not require the amount of amalgam that is typically contained in the ampoule. Because 70 percent of all fillings are replacements of previous fillings, additional amalgam is lost by the removal of the old amalgam (Concorde East/West Sprl, 2012, p. 9).

Mercury waste related to amalgam is found in various forms. Wastewater containing mercury is collected in filters inserted in water lines, collected by amalgam separators, or sent directly to municipal facilities for further treatment. Solid biomedical waste or hazardous wastes generated by the office are collected and sent to hazardous waste landfills where the mercury is stored so that it is not emitted into the environment. Municipal waste facilities typically are able to remove about 90 percent of the mercury amalgam from wastewater (U.S. Environmental Protection Agency, 2012c). Based on available data, about 38 t of mercury was released into the environment, recycled, or stored annually (Cain and others, 2007). Mercury emissions generated in 2009 in the United States from the dental sector include 24 t of mercury emitted into the soil, 4 t emitted into the air, and 0.5 t entered into water systems. An additional 6 t of mercury was recycled, and 3.5 t was treated or stored in hazardous waste landfills.

An additional potential source of mercury contamination is dental amalgam found in the mouths of deceased persons. This source contributed to emissions of about 6 t of mercury to the soil and 2 t of mercury to the air in 2009 (Concorde East/West Sprl, 2012, p. 21). Mercury emissions from this source have been the subject of recent congressional hearings. Based on data from the Cremation Association of North America, the amount of mercury available from crematoria is expected to rise because of an increase in the number of cremations and an increase in the number of fillings per person cremated. One estimate suggests that mercury available from this source could increase from 3 t in 2009 to about 8 t in 2020 (Reindl, 2010).

Some dental amalgam settles out as a component of sewage sludge accumulated at municipal wastewater treatment plants. The EPA finalized rules in February 2011 that would reduce air emissions for mercury and eight other air pollutants from publically owned incinerators that burn sewage sludge to limit the release of dental mercury into the environment (U.S. Environmental Protection Agency, 2011). About 14 t of mercury generated at dental facilities was treated at municipal waste treatment facilities in 2009 (Concorde East/West Sprl, 2012).

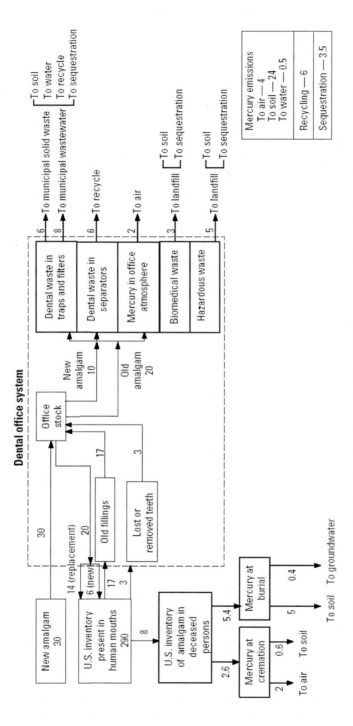

Figure 7. Material flow of mercury related to dental amalgam in 2009. Values are in metric tons. Adapted from Concorde East/West Sprl, (2012), except for emissions, which are from Cain and others (2007).

Other Mercury-Containing Products

Mercury can be found in discarded electronic components, particularly computer batteries, backlit liquid-crystal display (LCD) screens, switches, and circuit boards. The amount of mercury in a computer may vary from 50 mg to 45 g (New England Zero Mercury Campaign, 2002); new computers are likely to contain less mercury. More than half of these electronic components are exported to Asia for recycling (O'Connell, 2004). Because mercury is often included in the "other metals" category of material recovered from computers and electronics when reported, information on the amount of mercury recovered from computers and electronics in the United States may not be accurate (National Safety Council, 1999).

A small amount of mercury is used in a variety of chemical products, including acids, alkalis, bleach, buffers, cleaning products, coating materials, dyes, fixatives, laboratory chemicals, preservatives, reagents, and stains. The content of mercury from mercury compounds, preservatives, and reagents is typically as much as 250 parts per million (ppm; Northeast Waste Management Officials' Association, 2008a).

About 0.9 t of mercury was sold in formulated compounds and products in 2001, 0.8 t in 2004, and 1.3 t in 2007 (Wienert, 2009). As of 2008, four States had in place restrictions on the sale and (or) distribution of formulated mercury-added products. A number of companies have begun phasing out the sale on some mercury-containing products. Use in this sector is expected to decrease as appropriate substitutes are developed. There is little likelihood of economic recovery of mercury from these sources because of the diffuse use and limited production numbers of mercury-containing formulated compounds and products.

EFFECT OF THE MERCURY EXPORT BAN ACT OF 2008 ON THE U.S. MERCURY INDUSTRY

Much of the mercury that is being exported from the United States comes from mercury that has been recovered from recycled products, recovered from closed chloralkali facilities, or as a byproduct of gold and silver mining. Imported material from any of these sources may also be recycled and re-exported. The MEBA prohibits the sale or transfer of elemental mercury by Federal agencies to other government agencies or private entities after October

14, 2008, and prohibits the export of mercury from the United States after January 1, 2013. Mercury recovered through retorting must enter long-term storage as hazardous waste if it cannot be sold domestically. Mercury-containing products and waste and mercury compounds are not included under the ban and can continue to be manufactured and exported (U.S. Environmental Protection Agency, 2012d).

Banning mercury exports is expected to result in surplus elemental mercury inventories and reduce the amount of mercury-containing material imported for recycling. The DOE is developing options for long-term storage of elemental mercury and estimated that a storage capacity of 10,000 t of mercury would be necessary to handle the U.S. mercury storage requirement (U.S. Department of Energy, 2011, p. 3). Because no storage facility had been constructed as of January 2013, the DOE has allowed facilities to register to store mercury on site. As of 2013, two facilities had applied for storage permits from the DOE (Cynthia Manson, Industrial Economics, Inc., oral commun., February 12, 2013).

The long-term storage program for mercury is likely to affect mercury recycling by consumers, nonprofit recycling organizations, local recycling facilities, and the six leading mercury reprocessing companies. Much of the mercury recovered from chloralkali plants that closed before 2013 was exported; mercury recovered from chloralkali plants after the effective date of the MEBA in 2013 will likely be nominal (Bruce Lawrence, president, Bethlehem Apparatus Company, Inc., written commun., September 20, 2012). Potential sources of mercury that may require long-term storage include mercury stocks in the National Defense Stockpile and stocks held by the U.S. Department of Energy, mercury held by the two chloralkali plants closed in 2012, two remaining chloralkali plants in operation, mercury derived from gold mining in Nevada, and mercury held by reclamation and recycling facilities. Figure 8 summarizes the principal stockpiles of U.S. mercury as of 2010, along with estimates of the amount of mercury retained at each location.

Mercury users or recyclers no longer able to sell mercury on international commodity markets would likely lose revenue that would be gained by the sale of this mercury. In addition, they would be required to incur the costs for the storage of any mercury that could not be used domestically. Historically, the industry has not charged any fees for storing mercury from recycling consumer mercury products, but the DOE is required to assess fees for mercury storage. The MEBA may result in recyclers passing on the storage costs to customers in the form of increased charges for treating or reclaiming mercury, which may reduce the incentive for voluntary mercury recycling and therefore decrease the amount of recycling that takes place (Carpenter and others, 2011).

After the export ban takes effect, a possible alternative would be to export mercury byproducts and waste for conversion to elemental mercury outside the United States rather than continuing the current practice of retorting these materials in the United States and having to store the recovered mercury. Calomel recovered from the domestic gold industry and the chloralkali industry is the most likely material to be exported (U.S. Environmental Protection Agency, 2009, p. 36). For example, Bethlehem Apparatus Company, Inc. is considering moving its calomel recovery plant to Mexico to recover elemental mercury from gold ores mined in the United States and Latin America (Bruce Lawrence, president, Bethlehem Apparatus Company, Inc., written commun., September 20, 2012). Global recovery from the gold and chloralkali industries would likely be restricted to a few processors because the technology for recovery is highly specialized.

SUMMARY AND CONCLUSIONS

Consumption, production, and disposal of mercury in the United States have decreased as a direct result of increasing, stringent regulations and technological advancements related to mercury use. More than 20 Federal laws, rules, and regulations affecting mercury use have been enacted since 1970. The distribution of mercury use has changed significantly through regulation (paint and batteries), voluntary reduction by consumers (chloralkali manufacturing), and technological advances (dental, lighting, switches and relays). As global concern and regulation make it more difficult to import, use, sell, or dispose of mercury, consuming industries must increasingly rely on recycled mercury for needed supply or find acceptable substitutes for mercury.

Primary mercury in the United States is derived as a byproduct of processing gold and silver ore in Nevada. Data suggest that the amount of mercury recovered from gold processing operations in the United States has decreased by about 22 percent overall from 2001 through 2011; the average amount of mercury recovered annually is estimated to be 96 metric tons (t). In contrast, mercury emissions from the U.S. gold mining industry have decreased by 95 percent since 2001 as a result of increased regulation and improved collection and suppression technology (Elges, 2011).

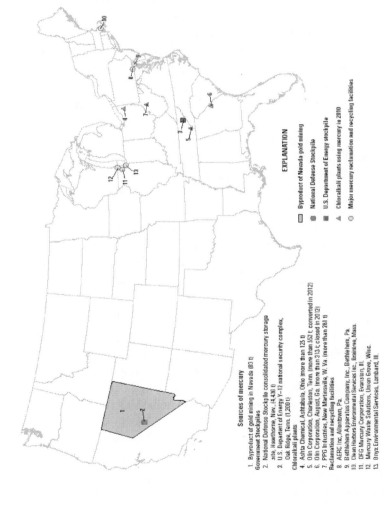

Sources of mercury

Byproduct of gold mining in Nevada (93 t)

Government Stockpiles

2. National Defense Stockpile consolidated mercury storage site, Hawthorne, Nev. (4,436 t)
3. U.S. Department of Energy Y–12 national security complex, Oak Ridge, Tenn. (1,200 t)

Chloralkali plants

4. Ashta Chemical, Ashtabula, Ohio (more than 125 t)
5. Olin Corporation, Charleston, Tenn. (more than 552 t; converted in 2012)
6. Olin Corporation, August, Ga. (more than 313 t; closed in 2012)
7. PPG Industries, New Martinsville, W. Va. (more than 281 t)

Reclamation and recycling facilities

8. AERC Inc. Allentown, Pa.
9. Bethlehem Apparatus Company, Inc., Bethlehem, Pa.
10. Clean Harbors Environmental Services Inc., Braintree, Mass.
11. DFG Mercury Corporation, Evanston, Ill.
12. Mercury Waste Solutions, Union Grove, Wisc.
13. Onyx Environmental Services, Lombard, Ill.

EXPLANATION

■ Byproduct of Nevada gold mining

▩ National Defense Stockpile

▨ U.S. Department of Energy stockpile

▲ Chloralkali plants using mercury in 2010

◎ Major mercury reclamation and recycling facilities

Figure 8. Location of leading production sources and inventories of mercury in the United States in 2010. Data represent production levels or inventory estimates reported (in metric tons (t)) and do not include mercury releases to air, land, or water. Data are from The Chlorine Institute, Inc. (2009), U.S. Environmental Protection Agency (2010), Brooks (2011), and U.S. Department of Energy (2011).

The amount of new mercury used by the chloralkali industry, traditionally one of the leading industries that use mercury in the United States, has decreased by 98 percent from 136 t in 1996 (Sznopek and Goonan, 2000) to less than 3 t in 2010 because of increased processing and recycling efficiencies and plant closures or conversions; much of the mercury required for chloralkali production is derived from onsite recycling within the mercury-cell process. In 1996, 14 mercury-cell chloralkali plants were in production; in 2013, one or two mercury-cell chloralkali plants are expected to be in operation. Mercury air and solid waste emissions from chloralkali manufacturing have been reduced by about 85 percent from 2001 to 2008, but as plants are closed, mercury recovered from processing infrastructure of closed plants has been exported, making the United States a net exporter of mercury, even though no mercury has been mined in the United States since 1992. The Mercury Export Ban Act of 2008 (MEBA), prohibiting the sale, export, and transfer of elemental mercury in the United States after January 2013, is intended to limit mercury exports for unregulated uses such as artisanal gold mining in developing countries. Calomel produced from gold processing, often recovered by domestic mercury recyclers, may be exported for mercury recovery after the MEBA takes effect in 2013.

As the overall domestic use of mercury decreases and distribution in various products and devices has been reduced, the amount of mercury-containing old scrap generated from discontinued or discarded products has decreased from about 250 t in 2000 to about 72 t in 2010. In 2010, more than half the old scrap supply was derived from industrial waste generated from the treatment of remediated soils from a closed chloralkali plant, imported material, and mercury-containing waste generated from dental facilities. Available information suggests that, even though a significant percentage of this material is consumed, exported, or recycled, about 42 percent or 92 t of mercury scrap or waste was unrecovered, lost, or landfilled in 2010.

Regulations promulgated since 1990 to increase the energy efficiency of commercial and residential lighting have contributed to an average reduction of mercury use in general service fluorescent lamps by 77 percent since 1985, but have increased mercury use in general service fluorescent lamps by 6 t through encouraging the use of mercury-bearing compact fluorescent lights (CFLs) as a replacement for incandescent light bulbs. The growing market penetration of CFLs has increased the interest in recycling by the consumer, but recycling remains expensive relative to the price of the lamp. It is expected that light-emitting diodes (LEDs), which contain no mercury but are presently more expensive, will eventually replace CFLs in many applications.

The use of mercury in dental amalgam has been a source of growing concern and government investigation. Dental amalgam represents one of the leading uses of mercury in the United States at about 18 to 30 t annually and constitutes the largest amount of mercury in use in the United States. In 2009, an estimated 28.5 t of dental amalgam was released into the environment, 6 t was recycled, and 3.5 t was treated and stored in hazardous waste landfills (Cain and others, 2007; Concorde East/West Sprl, 2012). Principal sources of mercury-bearing dental waste include water sent to municipal waste treatment facilities, solid material collected in amalgam separators and recycled, and amalgam fillings contained in the bodies of deceased persons. Efforts are ongoing to research and promote the recovery of mercury from these sources.

Development of suitable alternatives for products and processes using mercury is ongoing. Mercury-free alternatives exist for most applications; costs are generally similar or higher than the mercury-containing product. In many cases, alternatives use less metal and more organic materials or electronics than their mercury-containing counterparts.

Much of the mercury contained in products that are recovered by municipal, State, or industry collection activities is recycled by one of six leading recycling companies that process this material and recycle the mercury for domestic use or export. Formal collection programs have been established to collect and recycle mercury from automotive switches, CFLs, dental amalgam, and thermostats. In spite of these programs, however, the overall recycling rate for mercury in products in the United States has remained low (at about 10 percent). Although reliable national statistics are not reported, the recycling rate for mercury worldwide is less than 10 percent. The DOE estimated that the average amount of mercury recovered annually from recycling operations in the United States at 62.5 t. Increasingly the U.S. recycling industry has been processing a significant amount of mercury-containing material derived from foreign gold mining operations or mercury-cell chloralkali plants that have been decommissioned. Since the European Union mercury export trade ban was enacted in 2011, some European companies have found it profitable to ship mercury-containing waste to the United States for elemental mercury recovery because they are unable to sell elemental mercury recovered within the European Union or on international markets.

Regulation of mercury export and storage is expected to result in surplus mercury inventories in the United States. Long-term storage of mercury from chloralkali plants, government stockpiles, and recycling industry stocks will be required after the MEBA goes into effect in 2013 unless mercury-containing products such as calomel are exported for foreign processing to elemental mercury rather than processing it in the United States. Costs attributed to long-term storage may affect the competitiveness of the recycling industry if consumers are unwilling to pay for increased charges for mercury treatment or reclamation. This in turn may reduce the incentive for voluntary mercury recycling and therefore reduce the amount of recycling that takes place.

Most mercury regulations relate to elemental mercury. There is still a considerable amount of mercury in use in the United States that is in the form of such chemical compounds as calomel or wastes, which are not covered by the MEBA. Therefore, exports of these materials may continue after 2012. Elemental mercury may be converted to nonregulated forms for export if markets for this material can be found and the cost to do so is less than the cost to store surplus elemental mercury. For example, Bethlehem Apparatus Company, Inc. is considering moving its calomel recovery plant to Mexico to recover elemental mercury from gold ores mined in the United States and Latin America (Bruce Lawrence, president, Bethlehem Apparatus Company, Inc., written commun., September 20, 2012).

CONVERSION FACTORS, DATUM, AND ABBREVIATIONS

Inch/Pound to SI		
Multiply	**By**	**To obtain**
Mass		
ounce, avoirdupois (oz)	28.35	gram (g)
pound, avoirdupois (lb)	0.453592	kilogram (kg)
ton, short (2,000 lb)	0.9072	metric ton (t)
ton (short) per year (ton/yr)	0.9072	megagram per year (Mg/yr)
ton (short) per year (ton/yr)	0.9072	metric ton per year (t/yr)

Temperature in degrees Celsius (°C) may be converted to degrees Fahrenheit (°F) as follows: °F=(1.8×°C)+32.

Temperature in degrees Fahrenheit (°F) may be converted to degrees Celsius (°C) as follows: °C=(°F–32)/1.8.

REFERENCES CITED

Artisanal Gold Council. (2011). Silver causes huge increase in mercury use in artisanal gold mining: Artisanal Gold Council, March 29, accessed January 23, 2013, at http:// artisanalgold.blogspot.com/2011/03/silver-causes-huge- increase-in-mercury.html.

Ashe, Mary, Chwastyk, Dan, de Monasterio, Caroline, Gupta, Mahima & Pegors, Mika. (2012). 2010 U.S. lighting market characterization: U.S. Department of Energy, Januuary, 87 p., accessed June 13, 2013, at http://apps1.eere.energy.gov/buildings/publications/pdfs/ssl/2010-lmc-final- jan-2012.pdf.

Association of Lighting and Mercury Recyclers. (2004). National mercury-lamp recycling rate and availability of lamp recycling services in the U.S.: Association of Lighting and Mercury Recyclers, accessed September 12, 2012, at http://www.lamprecycle.org/public/images/docs/ALMR_capacity _statement.2004.%20pdf.pdf.

Association of Lighting and Mercury Recyclers. (2012). Lighting, mercury, and the environment: Association of Lighting and Mercury Recyclers, accessed September 12, 2012, at http://www.almr.org/mercury.html.

Beazoglou, Tryfon, Eklund, Stephen, Heffley, Dennis, Meiers, Jonathan, Brown, L. J. & Bailit, Howard. (2007). Economic impact of regulating the use of amalgam restorations: *Public Health Reports*, v. *122*, no. 5, September-October, p.657–663, accessed August 27, 2012, at http://www.ncbi.nlm. nih.gov/pmc/articles/PMC1936958/?tool=pubmed.

Bethlehem Apparatus Company, Inc. (2012a). Materials processed: Bethlehem Apparatus Company, Inc., accessed July 24, 2012, at http://www. bethlehemapparatus.com/materials-processed.html.

Bethlehem Apparatus Company, Inc. (2012b). Mercury recovery/recycling service: Bethlehem Apparatus Company, Inc., accessed July 24, 2012, at http://www.bethlehemapparatus. com/mercury-recycling.html.

Bethlehem Apparatus Company, Inc. (2012c). Why recycle mercury?: Bethlehem Apparatus Company, Inc., accessed July 24, 2012, at http://www.bethlehemapparatus.com/ why-recycle.html.

Bowen, B. H. & Irwin, M. W. (2007). Basic mercury data and coal fired power plants: Indiana Center for Coal Technology Research Basic Facts File #2, March, 21 p., accessed December 17, 2012, at http://www.purdue.edu/ discoverypark/energy/assets/pdfs/cctr/outreach/Basics2-Mercury-Mar07. pdf.

Brooks, W. E. (2011). Mercury, in Metals and minerals: U.S. Geological Survey Minerals Yearbook 2010, v. I, p. 48.1–48.8, accessed September 12, 2012, at http:// minerals.er.usgs.gov/minerals/pubs/commodity/mercury/myb1-2010-mercu.pdf.

Brooks, W. E. (2012). Mercury: U.S. Geological Survey Mineral Commodity Summaries 2012, p. 102–103, accessed September 20, 2012, at http://minerals.er.usgs.gov/minerals/pubs/commodity/mercury/mcs-2012-mercu.pdf.

Brooks, W. E. & Matos, G. R. (2006). Mercury recycling in the United States in 2000, chap. U of Sibley, S.F., comp., Flow studies for recycling metal commodities in the United States (revised): U.S. Geological Survey Circular 1196–U, 21 p., accessed July 9, 2013, at http://pubs.usgs.gov/circ/c1196u/Circ_1196_U.pdf.

Cain, Alexis, Disch, Sarah, Twaroski, Cliff, Reindl, John & Case, C. R. (2007). Substance flow analysis of mercury intentionally used in products in the United States: Journal of Industrial Ecology, v. 11, no. 3, April 23, p. 61–75.

Carpenter, Cliff, O'Conor, Letitia, Elmer, John & DePinho, Darlene. (2011). Assessing the impacts of the Mercury Export Ban Act of 2008 on the U.S. mercury recycling industry, in Annual Radioactive Waste Management Symposium, 37th, Phoenix, Arizona, February 27–March 3, 2011, presentation 11163: Tempe, Ariz., WM Symposia, 14 p., accessed July 8, 2013, at https://www.wmsym.org/archives/2011/ papers/11163.pdf.

Chlorine Institute, Inc., The. (2009). Chloralkali industry 2008—Mercury use and emissions in the United States: Arlington, Va., The Chlorine Institute, Inc. Annual Report, 12, August, 11 p., accessed September 29, 2012, at http://www.epa.gov/region5/mercury/pdfs/12thcl2report.pdf.

Concorde East/West Sprl. (2012). The real cost of dental mercury: Brussels, Belgium, Concorde East/West Sprl, March, 59 p., accessed August 27, 2012, at http://mercurypolicy. org/wp-content/uploads/2012/04/real_cost_of_dental_mercury_april_2012-final.pdf.

Corbett, Thomas. (2005). Recovering mercury switches from cars—Where are we today, where are we going: Great Lakes Regional Pollution Prevention Roundtable, 21 slides, accessed August 4, 2012, at http://www.glrppr.org/meetings/newyork2005/presentations/8-25-1330-corbett.ppt.

de Guzman, Doris. (2011). Inorganics—Olin's exit of mercury cell chloralkali is positive for industry: ICIS Chemical Business, January 3, accessed July 9, 2012, at http://www. icis.com/Articles/2011/01/03/9426289/inorganics-olins-exit- of-mercury-cell-chloralkali-is-positive-for.html.

Elges, Michael. (2011). The regulation and control of mercury emissions from Nevada mining operations: Nevada Division of Environmental Protection, February, 18 p., accessed August 17, 2012, at http://www.awma-easternsierra.org/ images/Elges_Feb_16_2011.pdf.

End of Life Vehicle Solutions Corporation. (2012). Model for estimating population of mercury convenience light switches: End of Life Vehicle Solutions Corporation, accessed July 3, 2013, at http://elvsolutions.org/ ?page_ id=1298.

Fashion Jewelry and Accessories Trade Association, The. (2012). Button cell battery legislation—Mercury free: The Fashion Jewelry and Accessories Trade Association, July 11, accessed February 27, 2013, at http://www. fjata.org/press/mercury-free-button-cell-battery-info/.

Gheysens, Rik. (2011). Mercury in fluorescent lighting: Ceolas. Net, October 26, accessed September 6, 2012, at http://ceolas.net/Docs/HB_ MercuryInFluorescentLighting.pdf.

Goonan, T. G. (2006). Mercury flow through the mercury-containing lamp sector of the economy of the United States: *U.S. Geological Survey Scientific Investigations Report 2006–5264*, 5 p., accessed September 12, 2012, at http://pubs.usgs.gov/sir/2006/5264/.

Griesbauer, Laura. (2007). Methylmercury contamination in fish and shellfish: CSA Illumina discovery guide, accessed September 12, 2012, at http://www.csa.com/discoveryguides/ mercury/review.pdf.

James, John. (2005). Phasing out mercury switch thermostats, in Phasing out sales of & collecting mercury-added thermostats: Achieving mercury reductions in products and waste—Coordinating national and local government initiatives, May 23–25, 2005, Portland, Mass., session 2C presentation, accessed July 17, 2012, at http://www.newmoa.org/ prevention/mercury/conferences/reductions/toc.cfm.

James, John. (2009). Mercury-free button batteries—Their reliability and availability: Maine Department of Environmental Protection, January, 11 p., 3 appendixes, accessed July 24, 2012, at http://www.maine.gov/ tools/whatsnew/attach. php?id=365209&an=1.

Lovitz, S. B. (2006). Scales of responsible gold mining—Overcoming barriers to cleaner artisanal mining in southern Ecuador: University of Vermont Master's thesis, accessed July 7, 2013, at http://www.uvm.edu/~shali/ Ecuador- Gold.pdf.

Maine Department of Environmental Protection. (2005). Mercury use in button batteries—*A report to the joint standing committee on natural resources*, 122th Maine legislature: Maine Department of Environmental Protection, 186 p.

Matos, G. R. & Brooks, W. E. (2005). Mercury statistics, in Kelly, T.D., and Matos, G.R., comps., Historical statistics for mineral and material commodities in the United States: *U.S. Geological Survey Data Series 140*, accessed September 12, 2012, at http://pubs.usgs.gov/ds/2005/140/.

Maxson, Peter. (2006). Mercury flows and safe storage of surplus mercury: European Commission, August, 79 p., accessed September 12, 2012, at http://ec.europa.eu/environment/chemicals/mercury/pdf/hg_flows_safe_ storage.pdf.

Mercury Policy Project. (2010). Turning up the heat—Exposing the manufacturers' lackluster mercury thermostat collection program: *Mercury Policy Project*, February, 11 p., accessed July 17, 2012, at http://mercurypolicy.org/wp-content/uploads/2010/02/turning-up-the-heat-3.pdf.

Merritt, Cam. (2012). Difference between T8 and T12 lamps: Demand Media, Inc., accessed March 19, 2013, at http:// www.ehow.com/facts_6190508_ difference-between-t8-t12- lamps.html.

Miller, Glenn. (2007). Byproduct mercury production in modern precious metals mines in Nevada: U.S. Environmental Protection Agency, 16 p., accessed August 17, 2012, at http://www.epa.gov/hg/stocks/Byproduct% 20Mercury%20Production%20in%20Modern%20Precious%20Metals%20 Mines%20in%20Nevada.pdf.

Mudgal, Shailendra, Van Long, Lise, Mitsios, Andreas, Pahal, Sandeep, De Toni, Arianna & Hylander, Lars. (2012). *Study on the potential for reducing mercury pollution from dental amalgam and batteries—Final report*: European Commission, July 12, 245 p. (Also available at http:// ec.europa.eu/environment/chemicals/mercury/pdf/Final_report_11.07.12.p df.)

National Electrical Manufacturers Association. (2002). House-hold batteries and the environment: National Electrical Manufacturers Association, June, 21 p., accessed July 30, 2012, at http://www.nema.org/Policy/ Environmental-Stewardship/Documents/NEMABatteryBrochure2.pdf.

National Electrical Manufacturers Association. (2003). Button cell battery collection—Why it does not make sense: National Electrical Manufacturers Association, January, 5 p., accessed July 30, 2012, at http://www.nema.org/Policy/Environmental-Stewardship/Documents/ Buttoncellcollection.pdf.

National Electrical Manufacturers Association. (2005). Fluorescent and other mercury-containing lamps and the environment—Mercury use, environmental benefits, disposal requirements: National Electrical Manufacturers Association, March, 14 p., accessed July 30, 2012, at http://www.nema.org/Policy/Environmental-Stewardship/Lamps/ Documents/Lamp%20Brochure.pdf.

National Electrical Manufacturers Association. (2008). Recycling household CFLs: National Electrical Manufacturers Association, October, 7 p., accessed July 30, 2012, at http:// www.lamprecycle.org/public/images/ docs/Recycling%20Household%20CFLs.%2010%2008.pdf.

National Institute of Standards and Technology. (2012). Mercury thermometer alternatives: National Institute of Standards and Technology, accessed July 18, 2012, at http:// www.nist.gov/pml/mercury_alternatives.cfm.

National Safety Council. (1999). Electronic product recovery and recycling baseline report—*Recycling of selected electronic products in the United States*: Washington, D.C., National Safety Council, 47 p.

Nevada Division of Environmental Protection. (2012). Nevada mercury control program (NMCP)—*Annual emissions reporting*: Nevada Division of Environmental Protection, accessed September 26, 2012, at http://ndep.nv.gov/bapc/ hg/aer.html.

New England Zero Mercury Campaign. (2002). Menacing mercury product pushers: New England Zero Mercury Campaign, January 30, 18 p., accessed July 24, 2012, at http://mpp.cclearn.org/wp-content/uploads/ 2008/08/productpushersnationalreport.pdf.

New England Zero Mercury Campaign. (2005). Turning up the heat— Eliminating mercury thermostats from the market-place: New England Zero Mercury Campaign, February, 12 p., accessed July 24, 2012, at http://mpp.cclearn.org/wp-content/uploads/2008/08/ nezmcthermostatreportfeb2005.pdf.

Northeast Waste Management Officials' Association. (2008a). Mercury use in formulated mercury-added products: *North-east Waste Management Officials' Association Interstate Mercury Education and Reduction Clearinghouse fact sheet*, October, accessed July 24, 2012, at http://www.newmoa.org/prevention/mercury/imerc/FactSheets/formprods. cfm.

Northeast Waste Management Officials' Association. (2008b). Mercury use in lighting: *Northeast Waste Management Officials' Association Interstate Mercury Education and Reduction Clearinghouse fact sheet*, August, accessed July 24, 2012, at http://www.newmoa.org/prevention/mercury/ imerc/FactSheets/lighting.cfm.

Northeast Waste Management Officials' Association. (2008c). Trends in mercury use in products—*Summary of the interstate mercury education and reduction clearinghouse (IMERC) mercury-added products database*: Northeast Waste Management Officials' Association, June, 28 p., accessed July 24, 2012, at http://www.newmoa.org/ prevention/mercury/ imerc/factsheets/mercuryinproducts.pdf.

Northeast Waste Management Officials' Association. (2009). Review of compact fluorescent lamp recycling initiatives in the U.S. and internationally: Northeast Waste Management Officials' Association, July 23, 24 p., accessed July 24, 2012, at http://www.newmoa.org/ prevention/mercury/ lamprecycle/CFLRecyclingReport.pdf. Northeast Waste Management Officials' Association, (2010a). *Mercury use in batteries: Northeast Waste Management Officials' Association Interstate Mercury Education and Reduction Clearing-house fact sheet*, January, accessed July 24, 2012, at http:// www.newmoa.org/prevention/mercury/ imerc/FactSheets/batteries.cfm.

Northeast Waste Management Officials' Association. (2010b). Mercury use in dental amalgam: *Northeast Waste Management Officials' Association Interstate Mercury Education and Reduction Clearinghouse fact sheet*, June, accessed July 24, 2012, at http://www.newmoa.org/prevention/ mercury/imerc/FactSheets/dental_amalgam.cfm.

Northeast Waste Management Officials' Association. (2010c). Mercury use in measuring devices: *Northeast Waste Management Officials' Association Interstate Mercury Education and Reduction Clearinghouse fact sheet*, January, accessed July 24, 2012, at http://www.newmoa.org/prevention/ mercury/imerc/FactSheets/measuring_devices.cfm.

Northeast Waste Management Officials' Association. (2010d). Mercury use in switches and relays: *Northeast Waste Management Officials' Association Interstate Mercury Education and Reduction Clearinghouse fact sheet*, January, accessed July 24, 2012, at http://www.newmoa.org/prevention/ mercury/imerc/FactSheets/switches.cfm.

Northeast Waste Management Officials' Association. (2010e). Mercury use in thermostats: *Northeast Waste Management Officials' Association Interstate Mercury Education and Reduction Clearinghouse fact sheet*, January, accessed July 24, 2012, at http://www.newmoa.org/prevention/ mercury/imerc/FactSheets/thermostats.cfm.

Northeast Waste Management Officials' Association. (2012). Interstate mercury education and reduction clearinghouse (IMERC) mercury-added products database: Northeast Waste Management Officials' Association, accessed October 24, 2012, at https://imerc.newmoa.org/publicsearch/ NEWMOA_IMERC.aspx#/CustomizedSearch.

Nowak, Milton, and Singer, William. (1995). Mercury compounds, in Kirk, R.E., Othmer, D.F., Kroschwitz, J.I., and Howe-Grant, Mary, eds., *Kirk-Othmer encyclopedia of chemical technology* (4th ed.): New York, John Wiley and Sons, v. 16, p. 229–243.

O'Connell, K. A. (2004). Putting the pedal to the metal: *Waste Age*, v. *35*, no. 4, April, p. 79–85. (Also available at http:// waste360.com/televisions-monitors/putting-pedal-metal.)

Olin Corporation. (2010). Olin announces mercury cell transition plan and fourth quarter restructuring charges: Clayton, Mo., Olin Corporation press release, December 10, accessed August 7, 2012, at http://www.b2i.us/ profiles/investor/NewsPDF.asp?b=1548&ID=42374&m=rl.

Poon, Daniel. (2011). US states ban mercury in button cell batteries: HKTDC Research, accessed September 12, 2012, at http://product-industries-research.hktdc.com/business-news/article/Electronics-Electricals/US-States-Ban-Mercury-in-Button-Cell-Batteries/psls/en/1/1X000000/ 1X07KKJT.htm.

PPG Industries, Inc. (2012). 2011 annual report and form 10–K: U.S. Securities and Exchange Commission, February 20, 9 p. (Also available at http://www.sec.gov/Archives/edgar/data/79879/000119312512064763/d2 60697d10k.htm.)

Reindl, John. (2010). Testimony to the U.S. House domestic policy subcommittee of the oversight committee of government operations and reform: Washington, D.C., Mercury Policy Project, accessed August 27, 2012, at http:// mercurypolicy.org/wp-content/uploads/2010/05/mpp_ testimony_domestic_policy_may_2010_final_version1.pdf.

Simpson, Cam, and Walsh, Heather. (2012). The slippery metal: *Bloomberg Business Week*, May 28–June 3, p. 62–68.

Sznopek, J. L. & Goonan, T. G. (2000). The materials flow of mercury in the economies of the United States and the world: *U.S. Geological Survey Circular 1197*, 28 p., accessed September 12, 2012, at http://pubs.usgs.gov/circ/2000/c1197/.

Thermostat Recycling Corporation. (2012a). Just how many is 1.4 million thermostats?: Thermostat Recycling Corporation, accessed July 16, 2012, at   http://www.thermostat-recycle.org/news/13-just-how-many-is-1-4-million-thermostats.html.

Thermostat Recycling Corporation. (2012b). California DTSC thermostat collection report for calendar year 2011 activities: Thermostat Recycling Corporation, April 1, 86 p., accessed July 16, 2012, at http://www. thermostat-recycle. org/files/media/20120618093320.pdf.

U.S. Bureau of Mines. (1973–1996). Metals and minerals: *U.S. Bureau of Mines Minerals Yearbook 1971–1994*, v. *I*, [variously paged]. (Also available at http://minerals.usgs.gov/minerals/pubs/usbmmyb.html.)

U.S. Bureau of Mines (1993). Mercury in 1992: *U.S. Bureau of Mines Mineral Industry Surveys*, 11 p.

U.S. Department of Energy. (2009). Energy conservation program—Energy conservation standards and test procedures for general service fluorescent lamps and incandescent reflector lamps: *Federal Register*, v. *74*, no. 133, July 14, p. 34080–34179, accessed May 20, 2013, at http://www.gpo. gov/fdsys/pkg/FR-2009-07-14/pdf/E9-15710.pdf.

U.S. Department of Energy. (2011). Long-term management and storage of elemental mercury—*Final environmental impact statement*: U.S. Department of Energy EIS–0423, January, 2 volumes, accessed August 7, 2012, at http://mercurystorageeis.com/library.htm#final.

U.S. Department of Energy. (2012). Impact of amended energy conservation standards on general service fluorescent lamps—*Fact sheet*: U.S. Department of Energy, 2012, accessed August 7, 2012, at http://www1.eere.energy.gov/buildings/appliance_standards/residential/pd fs/general_ service_fluorescent_factsheet.pdf.

U.S. Environmental Protection Agency. (2006). EPA's roadmap for mercury: U.S. Environmental Protection Agency EPA– HQ–OPPT–2005–0013, July, 85 p., accessed September 26, 2012, at http://www.epa.gov/hg/ pdfs/FINAL-Mercury- Roadmap-6-29.pdf.

U.S. Environmental Protection Agency. (2007). Background paper for stakeholder panel to address options for managing U.S. non-federal supplies of commodity-grade mercury: U.S. Environmental Protection Agency, March 14, 20 p., accessed September 12, 2012, at http://www. epa.gov/hg/ stocks/backgroundpaper.pdf.

U.S. Environmental Protection Agency. (2009). Potential export of mercury compounds from the United States for conversion to elemental mercury: U.S. Environmental Protection Agency report to Congress, October 14, 106 p. (Also available at http://www.epa.gov/hg/pdfs/mercury-rpt-to-congress.pdf.)

U.S. Environmental Protection Agency. (2010). Regulatory impact analysis—Proposed national emission standards for hazardous air pollutants (NESHAP) for mercury emissions from mercury cell chloralkali plants: U.S. Environmental Protection Agency, November, [variously paged], accessed September 12, 2012, at http://www.epa.gov/ttnecas1/regdata/RIAs/mercurycell.pdf.

U.S. Environmental Protection Agency. (2011). EPA's final air toxics standards major and area source boilers and certain incinerators overview of rules and impacts: *U.S. Environmental Protection Agency fact sheet*, 5 p., accessed June 13, 2013 at http://www.epa.gov/airquality/combustion/docs/overviewfsfinal.pdf.

U.S. Environmental Protection Agency. (2012a). Frequent questions about regulations that affect the management and disposal of mercury-containing light bulbs (lamps): U.S. Environmental Protection Agency, accessed September 7, 2012, at http://www.epa.gov/osw/hazard/wastetypes/universal/lamps/faqs.htm.

U.S. Environmental Protection Agency. (2012b). Mercury: U.S. Environmental Protection Agency, accessed December 17, 2012, at http://www.epa.gov/hg/index.html.

U.S. Environmental Protection Agency. (2012c). Mercury in dental amalgam: U.S. Environmental Protection Agency, accessed September 7, 2012, at http://www.epa.gov/hg/ dentalamalgam.html.

U.S. Environmental Protection Agency. (2012d). Questions and answers about the Mercury Export Ban Act of 2008: U.S. Environmental Protection Agency, accessed September 6, 2012, at http://www.epa.gov/hg/exportban-ques.htm.

U.S. Environmental Protection Agency. (2012e). What are the biggest sources of mercury air emissions in the U.S.?: U.S. Environmental Protection Agency, accessed September 7, 2012, at http://publicaccess.supportportal.com/ics/support/kbanswer.asp?deptID=23012&task=knowledge&questionID=21198.

U.S. Environmental Protection Agency, (2012f). What are the connections between mercury and CFLs?: U.S. Environmental Protection Agency, accessed September 7, 2012, at http://www2.epa.gov/cfl/what-are-connections-between- mercury-and-cfls.

U.S. Food and Drug Administration. (2009). FDA issues final regulation of dental amalgam: U.S. Food and Drug Administration press announcement, July 28, accessed December 3, 2012, at http://www.fda.gov/NewsEvents/Newsroom/Pressannouncements/ucm173992.htm.

U.S. Food and Drug Administration. (2011). Dental devices— Classification of dental amalgam, reclassification of dental mercury, designation of special controls for dental amalgam, mercury, and amalgam alloy: *Federal Register*, v. *74*, no. 148, p. 38686–38714, accessed June 13, 2013, at https:// federalregister.gov/a/E9-18447.

U.S. Geological Survey. (1997–2011). Metals and minerals: *U.S. Geological Survey Minerals Yearbook 1995–2010*, v. *I*, [variously paged]. (Also available at http://minerals. usgs.gov/minerals/pubs/commodity/myb/.)

U.S. Geological Survey. (2012). Mercury statistics, in Kelly, T.D., and Matos, G.R., comps., Historical statistics for mineral and material commodities in the United States: *U.S. Geological Survey Data Series 140*, accessed November 5, 2012, at http://minerals.usgs.gov/ds/2005/140/ds140-mercu.pdf.

U.S. Government Accountability Office. (2005). EPA needs to clarify the types of mercury waste that can be treated and disposed of using the debris regulations: U.S. Government Accountability Office, 57 p., accessed February 6, 2013, at http://www.gao.gov/cgi-bin/getrpt?GAO-06-99.

U.S. International Trade Commission. (2012). International tariff and trade dataweb: U.S. International Trade Commission, accessed August 13, 2012, at http://dataweb.usitc.gov/.

United Nations Environment Programme. (2002). Global mercury assessment: *United Nations Environment Programme*, 258 p., accessed July 27, 2012, at http://www.unep.org/gc/gc22/Document/UNEP-GC22-INF3.pdf.

United Nations Environment Programme. (2007). Japan's current status of supply and demand of mercury, and activities implemented to reduce risks using the most advanced technologies: *United Nations Environment Programme*, 17 p., accessed August 24, 2012 at http://www.chem.unep. ch/mercury/Call_for_information/Japan-submission.pdf.

United Nations Environment Programme. (2011). Recycling rates of metals— *A status report: United Nations Environment Programme*, 57 p., accessed September 12, 2012, at http://www.unep.org/resourcepanel/Portals/ 24102/PDFs/Metals_Recycling_Rates_110412-1.pdf.

van Zyl, D. J. A. & Eurick, G. M. (2000). The management of mercury in the modern gold mining industry: University of Nevada, Reno, accessed October 21, 2012, at http://www. mines.unr.edu/mlc/mercurygold.pdf.

Virta, R. L. (2011). Asbestos, in Metals and minerals: *U.S. Geological Survey Minerals Yearbook 2010*, v. *I*, p. 8.1–8.5, accessed September 12, 2012, at http://minerals.er.usgs.gov/minerals/pubs/commodity/asbestos/myb1-2010-asbes.pdf.

Virta, R. L. (2013). Mercury: *U.S. Geological Survey Mineral Commodity Summaries 2013*, p. 102–103, accessed January 30, 2013, at http://minerals.er.usgs.gov/minerals/pubs/commodity/mercury/mcs-2013-mercu.pdf.

Wankhade, K. K. & Agarwal, Ravi. (2003). Usage and releases, chap. 1 of Mercury in India—Toxic pathways: New Delhi, India, Toxics Link, p. 13–35, accessed July 24, 2012, at http://www.toxicslink.org/docs/06035_publications-1-33-2.pdf.

Wienert, Adam. (2009). Trends in mercury use in products: Northeast Waste Management Officials' Association, meeting presentation, Boston, Mass., November 17, 13 p., accessed August 24, 2012, at http://www.newmoa.org/prevention/mercury/conferences/sciandpolicy/presentations/Wienert_Session3B.pdf.

Wilburn, D. R. (2012). Byproduct metals and rare-earth elements used in the production of light-emitting diodes— Overview of principal sources of supply and material requirements for selected markets: *U.S. Geological Survey Scientific Investigations Report*, 2012–5215, 15 p., accessed December 6, 2012, at http://pubs.usgs.gov/sir/2012/5215/.

Zero Mercury Working Group. (2012). Phasing out mercury use in button cell batteries: Zero Mercury Working Group INC 4 briefing paper series, 2 p., accessed September 12, 2012, at http://www.zeromercury.org/index.php?option=com_phocadownload&view=file&id=164:zmwg-inc-4-briefing-paper-series-phasing-out-mercury-use-in-button-cell-batteries&Itemid=70.

In: Mercury in the United States
Editor: Erica O. Gosselin

ISBN: 978-1-63117-592-3
© 2014 Nova Science Publishers, Inc.

Chapter 2

EPA's Roadmap for Mercury[*]

U.S. Environmental Protection Agency

Executive Summary

Overview

Mercury is a naturally occurring element. It enters the environment as a result of natural sources (such as volcanoes) and human activities (such as industrial combustion and mining). Mercury is widespread in the U.S. and global environment. Human activities have increased the amount of mercury that is available in the atmosphere; in soils and sediments; and in lakes, streams, and oceans.

Significant progress has been made to date to reduce industrial emissions of mercury in the U.S., as well as to reduce or eliminate the amount of mercury used in various processes and products. Most of the large industrial sources of mercury emissions are sites where mercury is emitted as a byproduct of combustion processes. Other major sources of mercury include industrial processes and products that use mercury deliberately, such as certain chlor-alkali chlorine manufacturing processes, batteries, lamps, and measuring devices such as thermometers. Mercury is also released through mining practices, sewage discharge, and metal refining operations. When mercury is

---

[*] This is an edited, reformatted and augmented version of EPA report number EPA-HQ-OPPT-2005-0013, dated July 2006.

used in a product, most releases occur during manufacturing or disposal. In the U.S., there are over 100 manufacturing processes that use some form of mercury.[1]

While elemental mercury is toxic to humans when it is ingested or inhaled, EPA is most concerned about methylmercury, as it is a potent form of mercury and it is the form to which humans primarily are exposed. Methylmercury can be formed from other deposited mercury by microbial action in sediment and soils. Once formed, methylmercury can be taken up by aquatic organisms and bioaccumulates up the aquatic food web. While all forms of mercury can bioaccumulate, methylmercury generally accumulates to a greater extent than other forms of mercury.[2]

Mercury Sources

The primary sources of mercury releases to air, water, soils, and sediments can be grouped into four categories:

1. New releases from naturally-occurring sources (such as volcanic activity and weathering of rocks)
2. Re-releases of historic mercury previously deposited through natural and anthropogenic processes in soils, sediments, water bodies, landfills, and waste tailings/piles (also called "reemitted sources")
3. New releases of mercury impurities from combustion of fossil fuels, and from smelting of metals such as gold and zinc
4. New releases resulting from uses of mercury in products and manufacturing processes such as chlor-alkali manufacturing

Exposure Pathways

In the United States, humans are exposed to methylmercury mainly by consuming fish that contain methylmercury. Aquatic ecosystems respond to changes in mercury deposition in a highly variable manner as a function of differences in their chemical, biological, and physical properties. Depending on the characteristics of a given ecosystem, methylating microbes convert a small but variable fraction of the inorganic mercury in the sediments and water derived from human activities and natural sources into methylmercury. Methylmercury is the only form of mercury that biomagnifies in the food web. Concentrations of methylmercury in fish are generally on the order of a million times the methylmercury concentration in water. In addition to mercury deposition, key factors affecting methylmercury production and accumulation in fish include the amount and forms of sulfur and carbon species present in a given water body. Thus, two adjoining water bodies receiving the same deposition can have significantly different fish mercury concentrations.[3]

While the primary pathway of human exposure to mercury is through eating fish containing methylmercury, individuals may also become exposed to harmful levels of elemental mercury vapor found indoors in work places and in homes. When exposed to air, elemental mercury vaporizes and can be inhaled. The number of individuals exposed in the U.S. in this way is very small.

Fish Consumption Advice

Fish and shellfish are an important part of a healthy diet, since they contain high quality protein and other essential nutrients, are low in saturated fat and contain omega-3 fatty acids. A well-balanced diet that includes a variety of fish and shellfish can contribute to heart health and children's proper growth and development. EPA and the U.S. Food and Drug Administration (FDA) have issued fish consumption advice to help consumers understand the connection between the risks of methylmercury and the benefits of fish.

Research shows that most people's fish consumption does not cause a health concern. Elevated methylmercury in the bloodstream of unborn babies and young children may harm the developing nervous system, impairing the child's ability to learn and process information.[4] However, certain sub-populations are at higher risk than the general population because of their routinely high consumption of fish and shellfish (e.g., tribal and other subsistence fishers and their families who rely heavily on locally caught fish for the majority of their diet). Mercury concentrations in fish vary widely. While local freshwater fish also contain methylmercury, the majority of fish species consumed in the U.S. are ocean species and the methylmercury concentrations in these species are primarily influenced by the global mercury pool. Fish that are higher in the food chain—such as king mackerel, swordfish, tilefish, and shark—have much higher methylmercury concentrations than fish that are lower in the food chain.

The major tool for reaching and educating affected populations has been through fish consumption "advisories" or warnings issued by states, tribes, and the FDA. In March 2004, EPA and FDA issued a joint federal fish advisory for mercury in fish and shellfish. The advisory provides advice for women who might become pregnant, women who are pregnant, nursing mothers, and young children.[5] Additional EPA outreach actions aimed at reducing risks from mercury are discussed in Chapter IV.

Continuing Research on Sources of Exposure

U.S. mercury deposition is from domestic man-made sources and from global sources, including natural, re-emitted, and international man-made sources. EPA has estimated that over three-quarters (83 percent) of the mercury deposited in the U.S. originates from international sources, with the remaining 17 percent coming from U.S. and Canadian sources.[6] These figures include mercury from natural and re-emitted sources. This estimate is based on an advanced, state-of-the-science modeling assessment of atmospheric fate, transport, and deposition of mercury. EPA's modeling indicates that a substantial variation in mercury deposition occurs across the U.S. with domestic sources influencing mercury deposition much more in the eastern U.S. and global sources being a more significant contributor to mercury deposition in the west, where relatively few domestic sources exist. The scientific community's understanding of mercury atmospheric chemistry is evolving and there remain uncertainties regarding the simulation of mercury in atmospheric chemistry models. EPA continues to work to advance the state of the science on mercury chemistry and fate and transport modeling.[7]

EPA has analyzed various scientific questions relating to the primary fish-to-human exposure route, including key scientific questions described in Chapter VI. EPA recognizes that there remain scientific uncertainties associated with some of these questions, and is committed to continuing to work to advance the science in these areas.

Reducing Exposure by Addressing Mercury Releases and Uses in the U.S. and Internationally

EPA's long-term goal is to reduce risks associated with mercury. EPA recognizes that to reduce the risks associated with mercury, the Agency must first understand what contributes to the risk and what the appropriate mechanisms of risk reduction might be. EPA will take action to identify exposed populations, minimize exposures through outreach efforts, and appropriately reduce anthropogenic releases. As part of its strategy, EPA will assess mercury sources of concern and will: focus on uses that would lead to risk, where cost-effective substitutes exist; promote reducing mercury in processes and products where benefits of such reductions would justify costs, even where cost-effective substitutes do not exist; and work to identify and encourage development of alternatives to essential uses of mercury that lead to risk. EPA will also work with its federal partners to address risks associated with management and disposal of excess supplies of commodity-grade mercury in the U.S. In addition, EPA will support the efforts of other countries to take action to address risks associated with global mercury pollution by developing and implementing partnerships with international organizations, non-governmental organizations, and the private sector.

Six Areas of Focus in EPA's Roadmap for Mercury

EPA's *Roadmap* focuses on six key areas, with the overarching goal of reducing health risks associated with mercury exposure. EPA will reduce risk by:

1. Addressing mercury releases to the environment
2. Addressing mercury uses in products and processes
3. Managing commodity-grade mercury supplies
4. Communicating risks to the public
5. Addressing international mercury sources
6. Conducting mercury research and monitoring

Success in reducing risks associated with mercury exposure and mercury pollution in the domestic and global ecosystem will depend on pursuing all six of these actions simultaneously. The actions described in the *Roadmap* will be implemented over a number of years. EPA will periodically assess progress and make needed changes based on new information, successful efforts, and emerging needs. EPA will report on its progress, as well as on any major changes in direction from the current *Roadmap*.

About This Report

Over the past decade, addressing mercury risks to the environment and human health has been a focus for EPA. International, national, and local efforts to reduce mercury releases and uses have grown and are yielding impressive results. For example, overall U.S. mercury air emissions have been reduced by 45 percent since 1990,[8] and mercury use in products and processes decreased 83 percent between 1980 and 1997.[9] In 1997, U.S. man-made emissions contributed to approximately 3 percent of the global mercury pool.[10]

In 1998, EPA issued a draft *Mercury Action Plan* for public comment as part of its effort to address priority persistent and bioaccumulative toxic pollutants. The Agency received extensive comments on the 1998 draft and held subsequent meetings with states and tribes, municipalities, industry, and environmental groups, including a series of "listening sessions" in 2003.

Stakeholders provided very useful input on those aspects of the mercury issue on which they believed the Agency should focus its efforts. EPA also created an agency-wide workgroup to develop a new action plan, now called *EPA's Roadmap for Mercury (Roadmap)*.

Major offices at EPA are continuing to work to better understand the sources of mercury and how it impacts human health and the environment. The *Roadmap* describes the Agency's most important actions to reduce both mercury releases and human exposure to mercury. Creating the *Roadmap* has enabled the Agency to maximize coordination of its many diverse efforts, with the goal of improving EPA's mercury program. In addition to providing a roadmap for EPA, this report provides important information about mercury to other federal agencies, to our partners in state, tribal, and local governments, and to the public.

Summary of the Roadmap

Human Health and Ecological Effects

Mercury exposure can cause a number of adverse effects on human health. These effects can vary depending on the form of mercury to which a person is exposed and the level and length of exposure. The primary way humans are exposed to methylmercury is through eating fish containing methylmercury. Research shows that most people's fish consumption does not cause a health concern. Methylmercury exposure can cause neurological impairment. The fetus and very young children are more sensitive to methylmercury than adults. Methylmercury in the mother's body passes to the fetus and may accumulate there. There is evidence in adults that the organic form of mercury, methylmercury, also affects other systems. Specifically, some studies suggest that prolonged exposure to methyl-mercury, especially at higher levels, can harm the heart, kidneys, and immune system. However, additional studies are needed to better categorize the effect of methylmercury on these health endpoints.[11]

In the United States, human populations most highly exposed to methylmercury are those that eat fish and shellfish containing methylmercury in excess of the recommendations contained in the joint U.S. FDA and EPA consumer advisory "What You Need to Know About Mercury in Fish and Shellfish." Fish and shellfish are an important part of a healthy diet because they contain protein and other essential nutrients. Although nearly all fish and shellfish contain traces of mercury, research shows that most people's fish consumption does not cause a health concern. However, elevated levels of methylmercury in the bloodstream of unborn babies and young children may harm the developing nervous system, impairing the child's ability to learn and process information.[12] Fish that are higher in the food chain—such as king mackerel, swordfish, tilefish, and shark—have higher methylmercury concentrations than fish that are lower on the food chain. Mercury concentrations in commercial fish vary widely.[13] The majority of fish species consumed in the U.S. are ocean species and the methylmercury concentrations in these species are primarily influenced by the global mercury pool.[14]

While the primary pathway of human exposure to mercury is through eating fish containing methylmercury, individuals may also become exposed to harmful levels of elemental mercury vapor found indoors in workplaces and in homes. When exposed to air, elemental mercury vaporizes and can be inhaled. The number of individuals exposed in the U.S. in this way is very small.

Fish-eating birds and mammals and their predators are at risk for greater exposure to mercury than other animals. Methylmercury has been found in eagles, otters, and endangered Florida panthers.[15] Depending on the level of exposure, effects of methylmercury exposure on wildlife can include mortality, reduced fertility, slower growth, and abnormal behavior that affects survival.[16] Fish development and reproduction may also be altered by the levels of methylmercury found in water ecosystems.

I. Addressing Mercury Releases

Air

Addressing mercury releases to the air is important because mercury in the air can be deposited to water, converted to methylmercury, and taken up by fish. The U.S. has made significant progress in the reduction of industrial emissions of mercury to the air. In the last 15 years, EPA has focused most of its mercury reduction efforts on large point sources of air emissions, such as municipal waste combustors, medical waste incinerators, hazardous waste combustors, and more recently, industrial boilers and chlor-alkali facilities. With the March 2005 completion of final regulations for coal-fired power plants, the Agency now has Clean Air Act (CAA) standards in place limiting mercury air releases from most major known industrial sources in the U.S.

In addition to implementing these standards, the Agency, under the CAA Area Source program, is in the process of addressing certain smaller point sources that emit mercury.[17] Under the CAA Residual Risk program,[18] the

Agency is evaluating the remaining risks, if any, from sources for which EPA has previously issued emissions standards under CAA §112(d). Mercury is one of several hazardous air pollutants that EPA will be investigating under these programs.

Water

The majority of mercury in U.S. waters, particularly in the eastern U.S., results from air deposition from a variety of sources including man-made, natural reemitted legacy mercury, and global deposition.[19] States, tribes, and EPA's air and water programs are working together to address mercury air deposition issues that affect water quality and mercury concentrations in fish. EPA has strengthened its modeling tools to better identify sources of mercury deposition; relate changes in air deposition to mercury concentrations in fish; and ultimately determine the best mercury reduction strategies. EPA will continue to further characterize mercury discharges to water and will issue guidance on implementation of its methylmercury water quality criterion. EPA will work with its partners to develop tools and approaches for identifying mercury impairments and developing mercury total maximum daily loads (TMDLs) in water bodies.

Mercury can also be released directly to water from wastewater treatment plants, industrial facilities, and from current and historic mining activities (particularly in the western U.S.). The Association of Metropolitan Sewerage Agencies (AMSA, now known as the National Association of Clean Water Agencies) estimated that about 36 percent of mercury entering publicly owned treatment works is discharged from dental offices due to mercury in waste dental amalgam. Mercury discharges from dental offices far exceeded all other commercial and residential sources, each of which was below 10 percent.[20] EPA regions and states are working with dental offices to encourage collection of dental amalgam before it enters the waste stream. In addition, wastewater treatment plants are beginning to implement best management practices for collecting mercury from other industrial sources. EPA is providing guidance to wastewater treatment plants on how to characterize sources of mercury to the collection system and how to develop mercury minimization measures where appropriate. Mercury in the wastewater collection systems may come from the medical sector, dental offices, schools, and certain industries. EPA and the states also are modifying surface water discharge permits to incorporate more stringent requirements in mercury discharges, where appropriate.

Land

Mining is the largest source of mercury releases directly to the land in the U.S.[21] Mining releases occur as a result of existing mining operations for gold, zinc, and silver; the smelting of zinc and other metals and runoff from waste tailings; and from abandoned gold, silver, and mercury mines. The Toxics Release Inventory (TRI) reporting indicates these types of releases to land are large in scope and appear to be increasing. Of the 5.14 million pounds of mercury released to land, 1.4 million pounds is placed in surface impoundments and 3.7 million pounds is placed directly on the land in waste piles. Less than 1,000 pounds goes to landfills.[22] Most of these releases are not generally considered as environmentally harmful as releases to air, however, because the mercury may be less mobile and less likely to reach surface waters and fish.

However, in certain areas of the western U.S., mining runoff/erosion to sediments can be the primary source of mercury in fish in local waters. The 2004 TRI data indicate increases in reported releases from mining.[23] For more details on the TRI, see Section I, Addressing Mercury Releases. As a result, EPA is placing a higher priority on efforts to understand the risk associated with mercury releases to land from mining and take appropriate action.

II. Addressing Mercury Uses in Products and Processes

Addressing uses of mercury in products and industrial processes is a component of preventing human exposure from mercury releases to air, water, and land. Historically, the largest U.S. uses of mercury were in batteries, chlor-alkali manufacturing, and paint.[24] Mercury use has now been eliminated in most batteries and in paint. Today in the U.S. the largest industrial use of mercury continues to be in chlor-alkali manufacturing, while the dominant uses in products are in electrical and measuring devices.[25]

Many states, tribes, and local governments have been leaders in reducing mercury use. States have passed legislation calling for restrictions, bans, and labeling of mercury-containing products, as well as the removal and collection of mercury containing devices from the waste stream. States and local governments continue to initiate their own use reduction and collection programs from schools, hospitals, and laboratories to encourage the proper disposal and recycling of mercury.

EPA's long-term goal is to reduce risks associated with mercury. EPA recognizes that to reduce the risk associated with mercury, the Agency must first understand what contributes to the risk and what the appropriate mechanisms of risk reduction might be. EPA will take action to identify exposed populations, minimize exposures through outreach efforts, and appropriately reduce anthropogenic releases. As part of its strategy, EPA will assess mercury sources of concern and will: focus on uses that would lead to risk, where cost-effective substitutes exist; promote reducing mercury in processes and products where benefits of such reductions would justify the costs, even where cost-effective substitutes do not exist; and work to identify and encourage development of alternatives to essential uses of mercury that lead to risk. EPA will also work with its federal partners to address risks associated with management and disposal of excess supplies of commodity-grade mercury in the U.S.

EPA will explore both regulatory and voluntary programs looking at substitutes for mercury in products. The Agency will promote the procurement of non-mercury products by federal agencies. EPA is building a national database of information on mercury use in products. EPA will continue its successful voluntary partnerships, such as the Hospitals for a Healthy Environment program—its project with the health care industry to eliminate the use and purchase of mercury-containing medical devices and instruments.[26] The Agency also will continue to work with the U.S. Chlorine Institute to monitor mercury use in the remaining mercury-cell chlor-alkali plants in the U.S.

III. Managing Commodity-Grade Mercury Supplies

Elemental mercury is used in many products and processes, and is sold as a commodity on the global market. In recent years, approximately one-half of the current world mercury supply has come from mercury mines in Spain, Algeria, and Kyrgyzstan. (The Spanish mine has recently ceased mining operations.) The other half comes from the recycling of mercury from discarded mercury-containing products and other wastes, mercury recovered as a byproduct from mining of gold and other metals, and mercury supplies from the closure of mercury-cell chlor-alkali plants.[27]

As industry finds alternatives to uses of mercury, and as mercury-cell chlor-alkali plants phase out the use of mercury in their processes, EPA expects that there will be an excess supply of elemental commodity-grade mercury on the global market in the near future. As a result, there will be an increasing need for safe storage of excess mercury supplies.

Many states and local governments are now encouraging public and private collection programs for both bulk elemental mercury and discarded mercury containing products. The Environmental Council of the States (ECOS) has indicated that states do not have the resources or desire to store surplus mercury, and are looking to the federal government to address this issue.[28]

The issue of whether the federal government, states, or the private sector should take responsibility for storing commodity grade mercury supplies is an important and complex policy decision. In 2006, EPA will work with other federal agencies to initiate a process with technical experts and interested parties to discuss options for addressing the expected mercury surplus. EPA continues to evaluate options for disposal of mercury supplies, and published a report in April 2005 on the technical and economic feasibility of selected land disposal technologies in a monofill.[29]

IV. Communicating to the Public about Mercury Exposure Risks

The Agency will increase its risk communication and outreach activities to help people avoid or reduce their exposure to mercury. In the U.S., the greatest mercury exposure to the general population is from eating fish and shellfish containing high levels of methylmercury. Fetuses, nursing infants, and young children are at greatest risk because of their developing nervous systems. The primary tool for reaching and educating affected populations has been through fish consumption advisories issued by states and tribes. In addition, in 2004, EPA and FDA issued a joint fish consumption advisory for mercury that helps consumers understand the benefits of fish consumption, the risks of consumption to certain sub-populations, and mercury levels in certain fish.[30]

Many consumers are not aware of potential indoor mercury risks in schools, homes, and the workplace. Misuse or accidental breakage of some products can create indoor air health risks and exposure to dangerous levels of mercury.

The Agency will make it a priority to provide consumers with reliable risk information about mercury exposure so that they can make informed choices about the fish they eat and the products they use. EPA's most recent effort has been the January 2005 launching of its consolidated website on mercury.[31] The Agency will develop informational materials; support and build upon existing state, tribal, and local outreach campaigns; and maintain its centralized mercury website with helpful information on all aspects of mercury. EPA will also conduct public awareness evaluations of the effectiveness of existing outreach campaigns.

V. International Mercury Sources

EPA has estimated that over three-quarters (83 percent) of the mercury deposited in the U.S. originates from international sources, with the remaining 17 percent coming from U.S. and Canadian sources. These figures include mercury from natural and re-emitted sources. This estimate is based on an advanced, state-of-the-science modeling assessment of atmospheric fate, transport, and deposition of mercury. EPA's air quality modeling indicates that a substantial variation in mercury deposition occurs across the U.S., with domestic sources influencing mercury deposition much more in the eastern U.S. and global sources being a more significant contributor to mercury deposition in the west, where relatively few domestic sources exist.[32] The scientific community's understanding of mercury atmospheric chemistry is evolving and there remain uncertainties regarding the simulation of mercury in atmospheric chemistry models. EPA continues to work to advance the state of the science on mercury chemistry and fate and transport modeling. A number of key international emission sources contribute to global cycling and deposition of mercury via air pathways, including: coal-fired combustion sources; mining and metals production, such as smelting; mercury-cell chlor-alkali manufacturing facilities; and combustion or incineration of waste products containing mercury.[33]

EPA is currently participating in a wide range of bilateral, regional, and international programs and agreements to address mercury releases and uses and the resulting exposure around the globe. At the twenty-third session of the UNEP Governing Council, which was held in Nairobi, Kenya, February 21–25, 2005, delegates agreed to further develop the UNEP Mercury Program and to support the efforts of countries to take action to address global mercury pollution. Governments agreed to develop and implement partnerships with international organizations, non-governmental organizations, and the private sector to reduce the risks that result from the release of mercury to the environment. The partnerships created will leverage resources, technical expertise, technology transfer, and information exchanges to provide immediate, effective action that will result in tangible reductions of mercury use and emissions.[34]

EPA is building on existing bilateral, multilateral, and international agreements. In addition, EPA will build collaborative partnerships under UNEP with industries and environmental groups to bring technical expertise and assistance to address the global mercury problem. EPA plans to work with its international partners to reduce risks associated with mercury emissions from large point sources such as coal-fired power plants, chlor-alkali facilities, and artisanal gold mining; to reduce mercury use in products internationally (including mercury-containing batteries) where there are costeffective opportunities to reduce risk; to increase risk communication; to address the issue of commodity-grade mercury on the international market; and to research global fate and transport of mercury.

VI. Conducting Mercury Research and Monitoring

In 2000, EPA's Office of Research and Development (ORD) published its *Mercury Research Strategy*,[35] which outlined a strategic approach for the Agency's mercury research program. The purpose of the Agency's mercury research is to develop information that will reduce scientific uncertainties currently limiting the Agency's ability to assess and manage risks posed by mercury and methylmercury.

Research results support EPA's air, water, waste, and toxics programs in their ongoing regulatory and non-regulatory efforts to address mercury. ORD will continue to pursue its long-term goals to reduce health risks associated with mercury and to better understand the transport and fate of mercury in the environment. The major near-term emphasis of the mercury research program will continue to be focused on science and technology related to the control of coal-fired power plant mercury emissions.

In addition to research, scientifically sound mercury monitoring programs are essential for assessing the effectiveness of current regulatory and voluntary programs and for tracking health and environmental trends. Much progress has been made in recent years by EPA and others to establish routine monitoring and reporting systems to collect data on mercury releases and contamination. EPA is continuing to track and report data on mercury in four areas: air emissions, ambient air, air deposition, and fish tissue. The Agency will utilize the Centers for Disease Control and Prevention (CDC) data on mercury in human blood and hair samples. EPA will also continue to work with others to monitor other mercury releases and ambient concentrations. The Agency plans to use various existing databases for tracking overall progress in reducing mercury exposure. In addition, EPA will continue to seek improvement in monitoring methods and databases for mercury.

INTRODUCTION

Mercury is a naturally occurring element. It enters the environment as a result of natural sources (such as volcanoes) and human activities (such as industrial combustion and mining). Mercury is widespread in the U.S. and global environment. Human activities have increased the amount of mercury that is available in the atmosphere; in soils and sediments; and in lakes, streams, and oceans.

While elemental mercury is toxic to humans when it is ingested or inhaled, EPA is most concerned about methylmercury, as it is a potent form of mercury and it is the form to which humans primarily are exposed. Methylmercury can be formed from other deposited mercury by microbial action in sediment and soils. Once formed, methylmercury can be taken up by aquatic organisms and bioaccumulates up the aquatic food web. While all forms of mercury can bioaccumulate, methylmercury generally accumulates to a greater extent than other forms of mercury.

Methylmercury accumulates in fish tissue, which may then be consumed by people and wildlife. Mercury concentrations in fish vary widely. Fish that are higher in the food chain—such as king mackerel, swordfish, tilefish, and shark—have much higher methylmercury concentrations than fish that are lower on the food chain. The majority of fish species consumed in the U.S. are ocean species and the methylmercury concentrations in these species are primarily influenced by the global mercury pool.

Local freshwater fish also contain methylmercury. States monitor their waters by sampling fish tissue for persistent pollutants that bioaccumulate. States issue their advisories and guidelines voluntarily and have flexibility in what criteria they use and how the data are collected. As a result, there are significant variations in the number of waters tested, the pollutants tested for, and the threshold for issuing advisories. Based on self-reporting, the national trend is for states to monitor different waters each year, generally without retesting waters monitored in previous years.[36] Forty-four states, one territory, and two Indian tribes have issued fish consumption advisories recommending that some people limit their consumption of fish from certain water bodies as a result of methylmercury found in fish.[37] Human-caused mercury emissions have dropped 45 percent in this country since 1990.[38] EPA has not monitored natural mercury emissions in this country, which may also have changed over the same period.

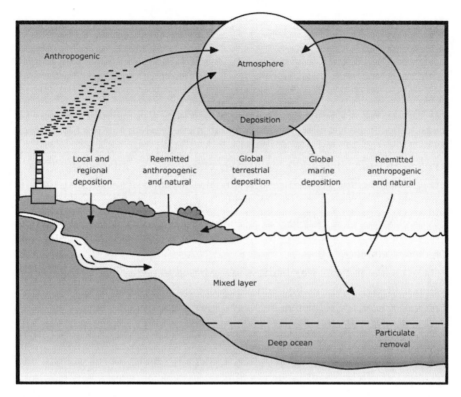

Figure 1. The Mercury Cycle.[39]

Mercury Sources

The primary sources of mercury releases to air, water, soils, and sediments can be grouped into four categories:

1. New releases from naturally-occurring sources (such as volcanic activity and weathering of rocks)
2. Re-releases of historic mercury previously deposited through natural and anthropogenic processes in soils, sediments, water bodies, landfills, and waste tailings/piles (also called "reemitted sources")
3. New releases of mercury impurities from combustion of fossil fuels, and from smelting of metals such as gold and zinc
4. New releases resulting from uses of mercury in products and manufacturing processes such as chlor-alkali manufacturing

Human Health Effects

Mercury exposure effects can vary depending on the form of mercury to which a person is exposed and the level and length of exposure. The primary way humans are exposed to methylmercury is through eating fish containing methylmercury. Research shows that most people's fish consumption does not cause a health concern. However, elevated methylmercury in the bloodstream of unborn babies and young children may harm the developing nervous system, impairing the child's ability to learn and process information. There is some evidence that exposures to methylmercury may result in genotoxic or immunotoxic effects. Other research suggests that reproductive, renal, cardiovascular, and hematologic impacts may be of concern. However, additional studies are needed to better characterize the effect of methylmercury on these endpoints.[40]

While the primary way humans are exposed to methylmercury is through eating fish containing methylmercury, individuals may also become exposed to harmful levels of elemental mercury vapor in homes and workplaces. When exposed to air, elemental mercury vaporizes and can be inhaled. Exposures from improper handling of mercury in schools, laboratories, and manufacturing plants; from accidental mercury spills; or in cultural and ritualistic uses can result in severe effects. Very small amounts of elemental mercury (even a few drops) can raise indoor air concentrations of mercury to harmful levels. The longer people breathe the contaminated air, the greater the risk to their health. At high exposures elemental mercury vapors can produce severe lung, gastrointestinal, and nervous system damage. The number of individuals exposed in this way in the U.S. is very small.

Ecological Effects

Birds and mammals that eat fish and their predators are at risk for greater exposure to methylmercury than other animals.

Methylmercury has been found in eagles, otters, and endangered Florida panthers. The 1997 *Mercury Study Report to Congress* provides some data that suggest some highly-exposed wildlife species are affected by methylmercury.[41] Depending on the level of exposure, effects of methylmercury exposure on wildlife can include mortality, reduced fertility, slower growth and development, and abnormal behavior that affects survival.[42]

Reducing mercury releases to the air is important because airborne mercury can travel short and long distances; be deposited on land and water resources locally, nationally, regionally, and globally; and lead to elevated methylmercury levels in fish. EPA estimates that since the beginning of the industrialized period, total global atmospheric mercury burden has increased by a factor of between two and five.[43] Figure 1 illustrates the physical cycle of airborne mercury from natural and anthropogenic sources as it is deposited to land and water and re-released.

U.S. mercury deposition is from domestic man-made sources and from global sources, including natural, re-emitted, and international man-made sources. EPA has estimated that over three-quarters (83 percent) of the mercury deposited in the U.S. originates from international sources, with the remaining 17 percent coming from U.S. and Canadian sources.[44] These figures include mercury from natural and re-emitted sources. This estimate is based on an advanced, state-of-the-science modeling assessment of atmospheric fate, transport, and deposition of mercury. Air emissions of mercury from combustion and industrial processes are the largest contributor to U.S. emissions. EPA's air quality modeling indicates that a substantial variation in mercury deposition occurs across the U.S., with domestic sources influencing mercury deposition much more in the eastern U.S. and global sources being a more significant contributor to mercury deposition in the west, where relatively few domestic sources exist. The scientific community's understanding of mercury atmospheric chemistry is evolving and there remain uncertainties regarding the simulation of mercury in atmospheric chemistry models. EPA continues to work to advance the state of the science on mercury chemistry and fate and transport modeling.[45]

Reducing Mercury Exposure

To further reduce risks associated with mercury, EPA's priority activities focus on six key areas:

1. Addressing mercury releases to the environment
2. Addressing mercury uses in products and processes
3. Managing commodity-grade mercury supplies
4. Communicating risks to the public
5. Addressing international mercury sources
6. Conducting mercury research and monitoring

EPA will continue to pursue regulatory and voluntary actions that will reduce risks associated with mercury. EPA's long-term goal is to reduce risks associated with mercury. EPA recognizes that to reduce the risks associated with mercury, the Agency must first understand what contributes to the risk and what the appropriate mechanisms of risk reduction might be. EPA will take action to identify exposed populations, minimize exposures through outreach efforts, and appropriately reduce anthropogenic releases. As part of its strategy, EPA will assess mercury sources of concern and will: focus on uses that would lead to risk, where cost-effective substitutes exist; promote reducing mercury in processes and products where benefits of such reductions would justify the cost, even where cost-effective substitutes do not exist; and work to identify and encourage development of alternatives to essential uses of mercury that lead to risk. EPA will also work with its federal partners to address risks associated with management and disposal of excess supplies of commodity-grade mercury in the U.S. In addition, EPA will support the efforts of other countries to take action to address risks associated with global mercury pollution by developing and implementing partnerships with international organizations, non-governmental organizations, and the private sector. As we work on these short and long-term plans, EPA will continue to work with federal partners to continue to educate the public about the risks of exposure from dietary and non-dietary sources.

State, Tribal, Local, and International Government Collaboration with EPA

In order to achieve reductions risks from mercury exposure, EPA will continue to collaborate with its state, tribal, and local government partners. As co-regulators with EPA, states have been actively engaged in a range of programs and partnerships to reduce mercury uses, releases, and exposure and to conduct mercury monitoring activities. In many cases, states and local governments have been leaders in mercury reduction efforts. EPA will build on these efforts and, where appropriate, help state and local governments replicate successful efforts.

In May of 2001, a coalition of state government environmental association leaders formed the Quick-silver Caucus (QSC) in order to provide a forum for states to work together, and with EPA, to develop collaborative holistic approaches for reducing mercury in the environment. In addition, the Environmental Council of the States (ECOS), an association of state environmental agency leaders, has passed a number of resolutions over the past several years that address mercury issues, many of which are also addressed in the *Roadmap*. EPA and states are continuing to work together on mercury issues under a cooperative agreement with ECOS.

EPA is also working with tribes to develop new activities that will help the Agency make progress toward attainment of EPA's long-term goals of "fishable waters" and "edible fish." Tribal community members who follow traditional diets and lifestyles may face greater risk from locally-caught fish than do members of the general population due to the prevalence of locally-caught fish and shellfish in their diets. EPA will work with tribes to improve the quality of water and sediments in order to improve fish tissue concentrations in tribal waters.

EPA will also continue to collaborate with other federal agencies involved in domestic and international mercury issues, including the U.S. Food and Drug Administration; the Centers for Disease Control and Prevention; and the Departments of Energy, Defense, and State.

In addition, partnering with the international community is of great importance to furthering global mercury reductions.

The majority of fish species consumed in the U.S. are ocean species and the methylmercury concentrations in these species are primarily influenced by global mercury contributions.[46] Also, even domestic freshwater and estuarine fish in many parts of the U.S. may contain methylmercury as a result of contributions from international sources in addition to domestic sources.

I. ADDRESSING MERCURY RELEASES

Overview

Significant progress has been made to date to reduce industrial emissions of mercury in the U.S., as well as to reduce or eliminate the amount of mercury used in various processes and products. Most of the large industrial sources of mercury emissions are sites where mercury is emitted as a byproduct of combustion processes. Other major sources of mercury include industrial processes and products that use mercury deliberately, such as certain chlor-alkali chlorine manufacturing processes, batteries, lamps, and measuring devices such as thermometers. Mercury is also released through mining practices, sewage discharge, and metal refining operations. When mercury is used in a product, most releases occur during manufacturing or disposal.

In the U.S., there are over 100 manufacturing processes that use some form of mercury.[47]

In the last 15 years, EPA focused most of its mercury reduction efforts on large point sources of air emissions such as municipal waste combustors, medical waste incinerators, hazardous waste combustors, and more recently, industrial boilers and chlor-alkali facilities. With the March 2005 completion of EPA final regulations for coal-fired power plants, the Agency now has standards in place limiting mercury air releases from most major known industrial sources in the U.S.

In the next 10 years, in addition to implementing the regulatory standards in place, the Agency's efforts to reduce mercury pollution will focus on three areas in particular: smaller sources and industrial uses that collectively contributed over 20 percent of the nation's mercury air releases in 1999;[48] understanding and addressing mining releases that in some areas of the western U.S. are the major sources of mercury pollution to water and land; and international emissions which continue to contribute to the mercury deposited in the contribute to the mercury deposited in the U.S. EPA's strategy for addressing these three areas will include, where applicable, a combination of regulatory and voluntary approaches to reduce mercury releases to air, land, and water, coupled with efforts to address the use of mercury in products and processes. As the U.S. continues to address domestic mercury use and releases, it will also promote international efforts to address mercury use and emissions abroad as discussed further in Section V on international mercury efforts. (Note: The *Roadmap* generally uses metric tons when discussing global mercury use and emissions. However, U.S. air emissions are reported in English tons. One English ton is equivalent to 0.9070 metric tons.)

Releases to Air

Sources. When the 1990 Clean Air Act Amendments passed, more than half of U.S. mercury air emissions came from just three source categories: coal-fired power plants, municipal solid waste combustors, and medical waste incinerators. The major air emissions source categories are shown in Table 1.

Progress to date. EPA's Clean Air Rules. Medical waste incinerators and municipal solid waste combustors are now subject to stringent control standards that require facilities to reduce mercury emissions by over 90 percent from 1990 levels. These efforts have contributed to reducing overall mercury emissions to the air by about 45 percent (from 220 tons in 1990 to 113 tons in 1999—see Figure 2).

EPA's recently promulgated Clean Air Mercury Rule (CAMR) is part of a suite of regulatory actions that will dramatically improve America's air quality. CAMR directly regulates mercury emissions from coal-fired power plants. Among other things, CAMR requires compliance with a two-phase nationwide cap on mercury emissions. The first phase cap (effective in 2010) is 38 tons per year ("tpy"), and the second phase cap (effective in 2018) is 15 tpy. Once fully implemented, CAMR will result in about a 70 percent reduction in mercury emissions from domestic coal-fired power plants, which is a reduction from a 1999 baseline of 48 tons.[50]

Table 1. National Air Emissions Estimates for Mercury[49]

Source Category	1990 (tons)	1999 (tons)[f]	% reduction
Utility Coal Boilers[b]	51.1	47.9[a]	6%
Industrial Boilers[b]	12.0	12.0	0%
Medical Waste Incinerators	49.7	1.6	97%
Municipal Waste Combustion	56.7	4.9	91%
Hazardous Waste Incinerators[b]	6.6	6.6	0%
Chlorine Production	10.0	6.5	30%
Electric Arc Furnaces[c]	6.9	NA	NA
Gold Mining	3.4[d]	11.5	NA
Other[e]	23.5	21.6	6%
Total	219.9	112.6	45%

[a] 1990 estimate derived using a different methodology.

[b] Regulations for these categories finalized after 1999.

[c] Electric Arc Furnaces data not available for 1999. The 2002 estimate is 10 tons per year.

[d] The 1990 emissions estimate is a preliminary estimate and is based on back calculations and assumptions using data from 1999 along with information about types of processes, production rates, and ores used in 1990 compared to 1999.

[e] Other includes, but is not limited to such items as, Portland cement production –2.36 tons per year (tpy), pulp and paper production–1.69 tpy, and over 219 miscellaneous industrial processes.

[f] 1 ton equals 0.9070 metric ton.

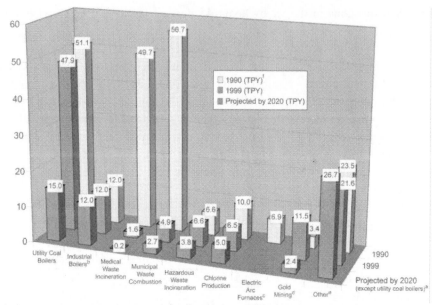

^a Fifteen tons per year will be achieved when full implementation of the Clean Air
   Mercury Rule is achieved, which may exceed 2020.

^b Growth in this sector is being offset by regulation.

^c Electric Arc Furnaces data not available for 1999. The 2002 estimate is 10 tons per
   year.

^d The 1990 emissions estimate is a preliminary estimate and is based on back
   calculations and assumptions using data from 1999 along with information about
   types of processes, production rates, and ores used in 1990 compared to 1999.

^e These projected emissions do not account for reductions from non-regulatory actions
   described elsewhere in the Roadmap.

^f 1 ton equals 0.9070 metric ton

Figure 2. Air Emissions Data for Mercury.

In addition to CAMR, the Agency recently issued another rule called the
Clean Air Interstate Rule (CAIR) that addresses the transport of pollution
across state borders in the eastern U.S. CAIR will result in the deepest cuts in
sulfur dioxide and nitrogen oxide emissions in more than a decade. Although
affected States retain flexibility to decide how to achieve the sulfur dioxide
and nitrogen oxide emissions reductions required by CAIR, EPA has
concluded that obtaining the reductions from power plants is highly cost-
effective. EPA therefore anticipates that affected States will meet their
emission reduction obligations by controlling power plant emissions through

the two-phase cap-and-trade approach provided in the final CAIR, the first phase of which occurs in 2010 and the second in 2015. EPA also concluded that the technologies that most cost-effectively achieve sulfur dioxide and nitrogen oxide emission reductions for power plants are scrubbers for sulfur dioxide and selective catalytic reduction for nitrogen oxide. These technologies, once implemented, not only reduce sulfur dioxide and nitrogen oxide, they provide important reductions of mercury emissions from coal-fired power plants. Thus, CAIR and CAMR work together and provide a flexible multi-pollutant approach for reducing sulfur dioxide, nitrogen oxide, and mercury emissions from power plants. From a legislative perspective, the President's proposed Clear Skies legislation, if enacted, would require a mandatory 70 percent annual cut in power plant pollution (NOx, SOx and mercury) when fully implemented.[51]

WHAT IS EPA'S NATIONAL EMISSIONS INVENTORY (NEI)?

Section 112 of the 1990 amendments to the Clean Air Act (CAA) presents a list of Hazardous Air Pollutants (HAPs), also called air toxics, which includes mercury and mercury compounds. In 1993, EPA began developing the National Toxics Inventory (NTI). This database has been expanded and is now called the National Emissions Inventory (NEI). The NEI is a national repository of emissions inventory data for HAPs. The emissions data and estimates cover major, area, and mobile sources, and include estimates of emissions at the national, regional, county, and facility specific levels.

The 1999 NEI generally serves as the national baseline inventory for this Roadmap because it includes HAP emission data supplied by 36 states in addition to data gathered while developing Maximum Achievable Control Technology (MACT) standards and Toxics Release Inventory (TRI) data. More information on the NEI, including summary data and documentation, can be obtained at http://www.epa.gov/ttn/chief/index.html.

In addition, §112 (f) of the Clean Air Act (CAA) required EPA to complete a Report to Congress that includes a discussion of methods EPA would use to evaluate the risk remaining after the application of Maximum

Achievable Control Technology (MACT) standards. These are known as residual risks. EPA published the Residual Risk Report to Congress in March 1999.[52] The Agency continues to evaluate the remaining residual risks, if any, for a number of source categories for which EPA has issued MACT standards. In the context of that review, EPA will evaluate the hazardous air pollutants (HAPs) emitted by each source category, including mercury.

Regional initiatives have also resulted in substantial reductions in air emissions of mercury. For example, EPA's Region 9 office and the State of Nevada entered into an innovative collaboration with four of the largest gold mining companies in Nevada to reduce mercury emissions associated with gold mining.[53] The Voluntary Mercury Emission Reduction Program set a goal to reduce mercury emissions by 50 percent by 2005, and has already surpassed this goal. In 2004, the program participants reported a 75 percent reduction from the baseline year. This is a reduction of 15,702 pounds of mercury from the baseline emissions of 21,098 pounds.[54]

Future focus. The Integrated Urban Air Toxics Strategy, which was published in the Federal Register in 1999[55], is an important element in EPA's national air toxics program. The strategy outlines actions to reduce emissions of air toxics, as well as assessment activities to improve EPA's understanding of the health and environmental risks posed by air toxics in urban areas. One major component of the Urban Air Toxics Strategy is the Area Source Program.[56] Area sources are smaller sources that can cumulatively emit significant amounts of hazardous air pollutants.

The 1999 Strategy identifies 33 hazardous air pollutants, including mercury, that EPA determined posed the greatest threat to public health in the largest number of urban areas. The Strategy further identifies 30 of those 33 HAP as being emitted by area sources. Finally, the Strategy identifies the 70 categories of industry sectors (i.e., source categories) that represent 90 percent of the aggregate emissions of the 30 identified HAP emitted by area sources. To date, EPA has issued standards for 16 of the 70 source categories and is currently collecting data and information for many other source categories.

Electric Arc Furnaces (EAFs)—one of the area source categories that the Agency is currently evaluating—emitted about 10 tons of mercury in 2002.[57] In EAFs, mercury is emitted through the stack when ferrous scrap containing mercury switches and other materials contaminated with mercury are melted. Many of these mercury-containing switches are found in scrap automobiles— over 200 million of these switches were installed in vehicles from 1974 to 2002. Although mercury switches were eliminated from new vehicles at the end of 2002, mercury switches will remain in the steel scrap supply for the next 10 to 15 years. The steel industry recycles about 12 to 14 million end-of-life vehicles each year, and vehicles retired in 2003 had 8.5 million mercury-containing switches.[58] The EPA air toxics program has identified EAFs as a priority sector and currently intends to propose emissions standards for that source category in 2006.

Releases to Water

Sources. The majority of mercury in surface waters from human activity in the U.S. is the result of air deposition, both from international and domestic sources. Mercury in surface waters can also occur naturally. Mercury can be released directly to surface waters from municipal sewage treatment plants, also called Publicly-Owned Treatment Works (POTWs), and non-municipal facilities (e.g., industrial and federal facilities). Point source discharges of pollutants to surface waters are required to have National Pollutant Discharge Elimination System (NPDES) permits.[59] On a national basis, these mercury discharges to surface waters are significantly smaller than nationwide inputs to water from air deposition. In some areas, particularly in the western states, mercury resulting from past mining practices (specifically mercury, silver, and gold mining) are significant sources of contamination to water bodies.[60]

EPA's Toxics Release Inventory (TRI) provides information on mercury releases to land, air, and water. (See box on page 27). Based on the EPA TRI data, total quantities of mercury discharged to surface waters have declined steadily from 2000 to 2004.[61] From 2000 to 2001 the decline was over 25 percent; from 2001 to 2002 nearly 32 percent; from 2002 to 2003 4 percent; from 2003 to 2004 nearly 59 percent and from 2000 to 2004 nearly 38 percent. TRI data for 2004 indicate that surface water releases of mercury totaled approximately 694 pounds (0.31 metric tons). An additional 219 pounds (0.10 metric tons) per year of mercury effluent is estimated from POTWs.[62]

Clean Water Act requirements. Under the Clean Water Act, states and authorized tribes must have water quality standards in place that define the designated uses and acceptable levels of pollutants for each water body under their jurisdiction. For mercury, EPA has published a national methylmercury ambient water quality criterion for protection of human health. This is a fish tissue concentration of 0.3 parts per million of methylmercury, based on EPA's 2001 Reference Dose (RfD) for methylmercury and consumption rates.[63] EPA's RfD is an estimate, with uncertainty spanning perhaps an order of magnitude, of a daily oral exposure to the human population (including sensitive groups) that is likely to be without an appreciable risk of deleterious effects during a lifetime.[64]

When pollutant levels exceed water quality standards, state water quality program managers must take action to reduce pollutant loadings. An initial step in this process is the development of a TMDL for a water body. The TMDL is the maximum daily amount of a pollutant that can enter a water body and still ensure that the water meets applicable water quality standards. TMDLs also allocate the allowable pollutant loads between the point and non-point sources of a pollutant.[65] Over 8,000 individual water bodies are identified as impaired (not meeting water quality standards) due to mercury contamination and will require mercury TMDLs,[66] and 44 states, 1 territory, and 2 tribes have fish consumption advisories due to mercury contamination.[67] States and EPA have been discussing how to best address mercury in their water bodies, since mercury can travel from sources out-of-state and from international sources and be deposited on local waters. Developing TMDLs that identify reductions from local sources alone is unlikely to result in attainment of water quality standards in many water bodies.

Progress to date. Because past analytical methods could not detect mercury at the level of current water quality standards in many effluents, there are limited data on low-level mercury discharges to water from point sources. To address the critical data gap, EPA recently developed a new more sensitive analytical method for use in water discharge permits.[68] As NPDES permits are reissued, they should require use of this more sensitive method where appropriate. Requiring use of this analytical method will improve EPA's understanding of the significance of point source mercury contributions to surface waters, and will provide necessary data for EPA and states to determine whether surface water discharge permits need to include mercury effluent limits.

As noted earlier, the states, tribes, and EPA's air and water programs are working together on how to address mercury pollution in TMDLs and water permitting programs, particularly mercury from air sources. To date, mercury TMDLs have been developed for over 250 water bodies in 19 states.[69] Many of these TMDLs identify needed reductions in air deposition of mercury. TMDLs such as those in Georgia and California also incorporate mercury characterization and minimization provisions for water discharge (NPDES) permit holders. To assist states in developing mercury TMDLs, EPA has conducted two pilot projects in cooperation with Florida and Wisconsin to examine approaches that could be used in developing TMDLs for water bodies impaired by atmospheric mercury.

Within the Great Lakes basin, the states have adopted water quality standards to implement the Water Quality Guidance for the Great Lakes System, including a mercury criterion of 1.3 nano-grams per liter (ng/l), based on protection of fish-eating wildlife.[70] Initial results in POTW effluent using the low level analytical method have averaged around 4 ng/l, and it is expected that most POTWs will not meet this criterion.[71] As a result, EPA expects the states in the Great Lakes region (EPA Regions 2, 3 and 5) will be utilizing statewide or individual variances from applicable water quality standards, which will involve setting mercury limits in NPDES permits based on a lowest technically achievable concentration, and requiring the POTW to implement a Pollutant Minimization Program (PMP) to address mercury-contributing sectors within its system. Region 5 has developed a PMP guidance document to promote a consistent approach to PMPs throughout its states.

EPA has provided sophisticated air modeling results to states to better identify the mercury contributions to water bodies from different air sources and geographic areas. The Agency has developed analytical tools that can be used to estimate the impact of air emission and deposition reductions on freshwater fish tissue concentration. These tools relate changes in mercury air emission and deposition rates to changes in mercury fish tissue concentrations.[72] By using such methods during the development of a TMDL, states may be able to determine how much of a reduction in air deposition is needed in order to meet water quality standards, and whether other actions in addition to anticipated air deposition reductions will lead to achievement of the water quality standard.

EPA's Toxics Release Inventory (TRI)

In 1986, the U.S. Congress enacted the Emergency Planning and Community Right-to-Know Act (EPCRA) and in 1990 passed the Pollution Prevention Act (PPA). Section 313 of EPCRA and §6607 of PPA require certain industrial facilities to submit reports each year on the amounts of toxic chemicals released or otherwise managed as waste. Amounts released are reported separately for air, land, water, and offsite disposal. The reported information is compiled and presented annually as the Toxics Release Inventory (TRI).

In 1998, several new industry sectors were required to file reports for the first time. The new sectors included metal mining, electric utilties and hazardous waste treatment facilities. These new TRI reports have improved EPA's understanding of releases of mercury and mercury compounds. In 2000, the TRI program reduced the use threshold that triggers mercury reporting from 10,000 pounds to 10 pounds. As a result, small users of mercury and mercury compounds are now required to report. TRI information and mapping capability can be publicly accessed at www.epa.gov/triexplorer.

In this document, "TRI releases" refer to quantities of mercury or mercury compound-bearing wastes that are released into the environment or otherwise disposed, and include, but are not limited to, releases to air, water and land, and to landfills, surface impoundments and underground injection. Even though disposals may be subject to regulatory and permitting requirements, disposal of mercury in waste to landfills, surface impoundments and underground injection is termed a "release" under TRI.

The Clean Water Act directs EPA to develop national technology-based regulations placing limits on the pollutants that are discharged by categories of industry to surface waters (termed "effluent guidelines") or to POTWs (termed "pretreatment standards"). Pretreatment standards ensure that pollutants do not pass through or interfere with the safe and effective operation of these POTWs. CWA §307(b) requires that EPA revise or establish pretreatment standards from time to time, as control technologies, processes, operating methods, or other alternatives change.[73] As part of its pretreatment standards review process, EPA is reviewing industrial sources of mercury for potential technology-based options for controlling mercury discharges to POTWs. In addition, POTWs are beginning to implement best management practices for collecting mercury from other industrial sources.

Many states have initiated efforts to reduce mercury in wastewater by focusing on the dental sector. Mercury in dental wastewater can be removed by relatively inexpensive amalgam separators and/or by using other pollution prevention practices. Amalgam separators currently on the market can capture more than 95 percent of the mercury particles in wastewater.[74] In addition to outreach and education to dentists on safe handling and disposal practices for mercury-containing dental amalgam, some local efforts are offering incentives to encourage the use of amalgam separators. For example, the city of San Francisco, California has a goal of installing amalgam separators in all 900 dental offices located in the city and is offering assistance and incentives to dental offices least able to afford the separators— specifically those serving low-income communities.[75]

Future focus. EPA will continue to work with its state and tribal partners to identify approaches to TMDLs for water bodies impaired by atmospheric mercury in order to make progress toward achieving state water quality standards. Potential approaches include regional-scale TMDLs and approaches which take into account comprehensive state mercury reduction programs.

Releases to Land

Sources. TRI provides the best single source of information on releases of mercury to land. Based on TRI,[76] the total amounts of mercury that were released to land decreased by about 18 percent between 2002 and 2003 (from 2,554 to 2,079 metric tons per year). Although these amounts are relatively large, based on existing information, such releases are generally not considered to be as environmentally harmful as releases to air because the mercury may be less mobile and less likely to reach surface waters and fish. Nevertheless, because of the large quantities of mercury in waste being placed on the land, it is prudent for EPA to conduct further investigations to determine the risks associated with these releases.

The vast majority of U.S. land releases are the result of mining activities. Mercury is no longer mined domestically in the U.S., but is a byproduct of metals mining, particularly gold mining. The 2004 TRI data indicate that 2079 metric tons of mercury were released to the land. Of that, 1.461 million pounds were released to "other surface impoundments"[77] and 2.620 million pounds were released to "other land disposal".[78] Three metal mining facilities accounted for over 74 percent of the total mercury land releases in 2004. The majority of TRI land releases is due to gold, silver, and zinc mining, and may continue to rise over the next few years due to increased gold production.

The Agency is beginning to investigate and characterize mercury releases and risks from mine tailings and mining processes, as well as other land releases. EPA plans to use the latest TRI data to evaluate trends for how mercury is being released to land.

A small percentage of releases to land reported in TRI are not related to mining activities. The majority of these releases is attributed to the disposal of mercury in waste in hazardous or non-hazardous regulated landfills or surface impoundments.

Progress to date. EPA has made substantial progress reducing the volume of mercury-containing devices disposed of in landfills since 1990. This progress is largely due to the Battery Act[79] which places limits on mercury used in batteries. The promulgation of the Municipal Incinerator Rules[80] also helped reduce the amount of mercury going into the waste streams by limiting mercury emissions from these incinerators, which in turn encouraged localities to begin collection and recycling programs for mercury-containing devices. The Universal Waste Rule[81] is another example of a regulation helping to facilitate proper management of mercury-containing devices to keep them out of incinerators and landfills. In August 2005, EPA finalized its proposal to add mercury-containing devices (e.g., thermometers and switches) to the federal Universal Waste Rule.[82] For these widely-generated hazardous wastes, this rule streamlines entry into the waste management system, encourages recovery and recycling, and keeps wastes out of the municipal waste stream. States and localities have made substantial progress promoting recycling of discarded mercury-containing products. Many states are also involved in banning certain mercury-containing devices and actively promoting the use of mercury substitutes, where available.

Future focus. Because there is a steady increase in reported land releases, the Agency will expand its efforts to better characterize and address land releases of mercury from the mining sector. The Agency intends to evaluate these releases to determine whether further action is needed.

Using the latest TRI data, EPA will continue to analyze long-term trends and monitor sectors that are not addressing their mercury releases to assess appropriate voluntary or regulatory avenues for addressing mercury releases.

EPA will continue to address mercury releases at remediation sites with significant mercury contamination consistent with the priorities set by the Superfund National Priorities List[83] and the RCRA Corrective Action baseline for high-priority facilities.[84] EPA will continue to coordinate with states to assist in cleaning up serious spills of mercury in order to protect public health. In addition, EPA is looking into mercury issues associated with abandoned mines relative to downstream water quality.

EPA will continue to work toward reducing risk associated with mercury from the nation's waste streams and from potential releases to land by promoting cost-effective reductions in mercury use in products and processes and by promoting the collection and recycling of discarded mercury-containing products.

State, Tribal, and Local Government Release Reduction Efforts

Many state, tribal, and local governments have been leaders in addressing mercury releases. States have developed innovative mercury release and use reduction laws and regulations that supplement, and in some cases provide a model for, national efforts.

For example, the state of Maine passed a law requiring removal of mercury convenience lighting switches from automobiles prior to crushing the automobiles for scrap metal.[85] The purpose of the legislation is to reduce mercury releases from Electric Arc Furnaces (EAFs) used to melt scrap metal for steel production. The source of mercury from EAFs has been determined to be mercury components contained in the scrap metal melted by such furnaces. Scrap automobiles are the largest mercury-containing feedstock for these furnaces.[86] Several other states are pursuing their own auto switch removal programs, including Pennsylvania, New York, New Jersey, Illinois, Colorado, Washington, Oregon, and Idaho. As a result of this state leadership, auto manufacturers no longer install mercury switches for convenience lighting and are actively investigating ways to keep mercury out of vehicles. In addition, EPA is engaging in discussions with various stakeholders, including auto dismantlers, shredders, steel makers, auto manufacturers, environmental groups, and states, with the aim of developing a collaborative national approach to removing mercury switches from the large inventory of autos in use today prior to their disposal, crushing, and smelting.

States, tribes, and local governments have played a key role in outreach to the business community and to the general public about the importance of properly disposing of mercury-containing products and about alternatives to such products. Many states and local governments have sponsored mercury collection programs for businesses and households. For example, cities such as San Francisco, California, and states, such as Florida and New Hampshire, are conducting outreach to dentists on the proper handling and disposal of mercury-containing dental amalgam, including efforts to promote increased use of dental amalgam separators that reduce the amount of mercury discharged into the POTWs from dental wastewater.

Priority Activities for Addressing Mercury Releases

- ***Standard for Coal-Fired Power Plants*** – On March 15, 2005, EPA finalized the Clean Air Mercury Rule which establishes standards of performance for electric power plants based on a market-based cap-and-trade methodology. This rule will build on EPA's Clean Air Interstate Rule (CAIR) to significantly reduce emissions from coal-fired power plants. The standards address mercury air emissions from new and existing coal-fired electric utility steam generating units. When fully implemented, these rules will reduce power plant emissions of mercury from 48 tons per year to 15 tons per year, a reduction of nearly 70 percent.[87] **Timeline: CAMR will reduce emissions from 48 tons to 31 tons beginning 2010 and declining thereafter until emissions are reduced to 15 tons when the program is fully implemented**

- *MACT Standard for Industrial Boilers* – EPA promulgated a MACT standard for mercury air emissions from industrial boilers in September 2004. This effort should result in a 17 percent reduction in mercury emissions from this sector since 1990. **Timeline: Implementation by 2007**

- *MACT Standard for Hazardous Waste Combustors* – In October 2005, EPA published emission standards for mercury and other hazardous air pollutants for incinerators, cement kilns, lightweight aggregate kilns, industrial/commercial/institutional boilers and process heaters, and hydrochloric acid production furnaces that burn hazardous waste. An interim standard that took effect in 2003 has already reduced mercury emissions from levels in 2000 for incinerators, cement kilns, and lightweight aggregate kilns. The final MACT standard is estimated to further reduce mercury air emissions from all hazardous waste combustors by an additional 39 percent (from 2.4 tons/year to 1.5 tons/year).[88] **Timeline: Implementation by 2008**

- *MACT Standard for Chlor-Alkali Sector* – In December 2003, EPA promulgated a rule to regulate emissions of mercury from mercury-cell chlor-alkali plants.[89] Mercury-cell chlor-alkali plants produce chlorine and caustic soda (used to neutralize acidic compounds) using mercury cells. The rule will also require rigorous work practice standards that will reduce mercury emissions from fugitive sources. Although EPA is not able to accurately quantify the reductions associated with these work practice standards, the requirements will reduce mercury air emissions industry-wide. **Timeline: Implementation by December 2006**

- *MACT Standard for Iron and Steel Foundries* – In 2004 EPA issued a final rule to reduce toxic air emissions, including mercury, from iron and steel foundries. Iron and steel foundries melt scrap, ingot, and other forms of iron and steel and pour the resulting molten metal into molds to produce shaped products. The rule includes emission limits for manufacturing processes and pollution prevention-based requirements to reduce air toxics from furnace materials and coating/ binder formulations. Implementation of the rule is expected to reduce mercury emissions by 1.4 tons—an 80 percent reduction from current levels.[90] **Timeline: Implementation by 2007**

- *Area Source Program* – Under the Urban Air Toxics Strategy, EPA is developing standards to control emissions of toxic air pollutants (hazardous air pollutants or HAP) from area sources. Area sources are those sources that emit less than 10 tons annually of a single HAP or less than 25 tons annually of a combination of HAP.

  The Clean Air Act (CAA) requires EPA to identify a list of at least 30 HAP that pose the greatest potential health threat in urban areas, and in the 1999 strategy, EPA identified 33 such pollutants. Of those 33 identified pollutants, EPA determined that 30 stem from area source emissions. Through three separate listings (including a list in the Urban Air Toxics Strategy), EPA has identified a total of 70 area source categories which represent 90 percent of the aggregate emissions of the 30 listed area source HAP. Of these 70 area source categories, 16 have been regulated, and EPA is currently collecting data and information for many other source categories. **Timeline: Ongoing**

- *Rule on Electric Arc Furnaces (EAFs)* – In 2006, EPA plans to propose a comprehensive rule for steel mills that use EAFs to address emissions of mercury, lead, and other metals and organic hazardous air pollutants. EPA will also pursue voluntary programs in parallel with the development of regulations to ensure mercury emissions reductions. These actions collectively should greatly reduce mercury air emissions from EAFs and other scrap consumers over the course of the next 10 years. **Timeline: Propose rule in 2006**

- *Mercury Automobile Switches* – Many pre-2003 domestic passenger vehicles have mercury-containing switches in convenience light assemblies and anti-lock braking systems (ABS). Building on and coordinating with successful state and local automotive switch removal efforts, EPA hopes to develop a partnership with automobile dismantlers, scrap shredders, steelmakers, and the automotive industry to remove mercury switches from scrapped autos in the U.S. prior to disassembly, shredding, and melting in steelmaking furnaces. **Timeline: 2006**

- *Characterize Mining Releases* – EPA is examining the issue of mercury-bearing materials being placed on land at active gold mines and any subsequent releases which are not covered by TRI (air, surface, water, or ground water) associated with that placement. An effort is underway to assess the releases and their potential impact to determine if further action is war-ranted. **Timeline: 2006**

- *Characterize Mercury Discharges to Surface Water* – As mentioned in the progress to date section, EPA recently developed a new analytical method for use in water discharge permitting programs that will improve EPA's understanding of point source mercury contributions to surface waters. Based on that information, EPA is providing guidance to Publicly Owned Treatment Works (POTWs) on how to characterize sources of mercury to the collection system and how to develop mercury minimization measures where appropriate. Mercury in POTW collection systems may come from the medical sector, dental offices, schools, and certain industries. EPA is continuing to explore opportunities for pollution prevention in the dental sector and other sources. **Timeline: Ongoing**

- *Issue Mercury Water Quality Criterion Implementation Guidance* – EPA currently intends to issue implementation guidance to states and tribes for the fish-tissue-based mercury water quality criterion and how to incorporate it into permits and TMDLs. Once states and tribes adopt the water quality criterion into their water quality standards, officials can incorporate appropriate controls where necessary into TMDLs and watershed management decisions. State environmental officials can incorporate appropriate controls where necessary into permits and enforce these requirements. **Timeline: 2007**

- *Improve Tools for Tracking Mercury in Fish Tissue* – EPA continues to improve its models for tracking methylmercury in fish tissue and air deposition trends.[91] EPA will also begin to estimate the expected effectiveness of proposed Hg source reduction activities in terms of reduced fish tissue methylmercury concentrations. This effort may involve the continued evolution of the Mercury Maps modeling framework, and its integration with sophisticated air deposition model outputs (e.g., CMAQ [Community Multiscale Air Quality]). In addition, EPA will continue to refine its air emission inventories to provide an assessment of emission reductions gained through implementation of its regulatory programs. **Timeline: To be determined**

- ***Develop Alternative Approaches and Tools for Identifying Mercury Impairments and Developing Mercury TMDLs***– EPA will work with states, tribes, and stakeholders to determine how best to use TMDLs to provide a basis for reducing mercury releases to water, including those from air deposition, to meet state water quality standards and Clean Water Act goals. EPA will provide updated mercury deposition modeling results to states for use in TMDLs, including the major sources of mercury deposition to each state. EPA will also evaluate approaches for identifying mercury impairments and developing mercury TMDLs, such as regional-scale TMDLs and approaches that acknowledge strong state mercury reduction programs, in order to make progress toward attaining state water quality standards. **Timeline: Ongoing**

- ***Promote The Proper Collection and Recycling of Dental Office Amalgam Waste*** – EPA is currently developing a dental office amalgam recycling program called its "gray bag" program. This program will assist dentists in properly collecting and managing dental amalgam wastes generated in their offices to minimize mercury releases to air, land, and water. This program also will ensure that dental amalgam is sent to responsible recyclers who can adequately minimize mercury releases by keeping the amalgam waste out of the wastewater stream and out of municipal and medical incinerators. **Timeline: In 2006**

- ***Fluorescent Lamp Recycling*** – EPA is administering a grant program to increase the recycling rate of mercury-containing lamps. Grants are used to create lamp recycling outreach programs targeting commercial and industrial users of mercury-containing lamps. State environmental agencies, tribes, non-profit organizations, lamp manufacturers, and recyclers are all partners in implementing this program. EPA is currently providing national coordination of these efforts as well as technical expertise on regulatory issues. EPA will build upon the results of this grant program to increase the national rate of bulb recycling. EPA is also working with Regions and states to develop guidance on the conditions under which drum top crushing of waste lamps can be permitted without unacceptable mercury releases or danger to personnel who operate the crushers. **Timeline: In 2006**

- *Analyze Sectors and Trends for Mercury Releases in the TRI/NEI Databases* – EPA will continue to evaluate the "other" smaller sources, as appropriate, that cumulatively release significant amounts of mercury to the environment. EPA will monitor existing data on how mercury is managed onsite and/or off-site and will examine potential sectors for expanding voluntary mercury reduction programs. **Timeline: Ongoing**

II. ADDRESSING MERCURY USES IN PRODUCTS AND PROCESSES

Overview

Addressing uses of mercury in products and processes is a component of preventing mercury releases to air, water, or land. These releases may occur during manufacturing and industrial processes, or during the disposal or recycling of mercury containing products and wastes. Addressing mercury use in products also reduces the demand for mercury by product manufacturers, thereby reducing demand for new mercury mining. Mercury mining still occurs in other countries and causes further releases to the global environment. Addressing demand for and use of mercury is critical to breaking the cycle of mercury being transferred from one environmental medium to another.

USES CAN CONTRIBUTE TO RELEASES

Mercury use in products can lead to mercury releases through:

- Manufacturing of product
- Spills/breakage
- Recycling/collection
- Disposal

EPA's long-term goal is to reduce risks associated with mercury. EPA recognizes that to reduce risks associated with mercury, the Agency must first understand what contributes to the risk and what the appropriate mechanisms of risk reduction might be. EPA will take action to identify exposed populations, minimize exposures through outreach efforts, and appropriately address anthropogenic releases. As part of its strategy, EPA will assess mercury sources of concern and will: focus on uses that would lead to risk, where cost-effective substitutes exist; promote reducing mercury in processes and products where benefits of such reduction would justify the cost, even where cost-effective substitutes do not exist; and work to identify and encourage development of alternatives to essential uses of mercury that lead to risk.

Sources. In 1980, the three largest U.S. industrial uses of mercury were in batteries (1,052 metric tons), the chlor-alkali manufacturing process (358 metric tons), and paint (326 metric tons).[92] Mercury use in products accounted for an estimated 245 metric tons in 2001. As Figure 3 illustrates, the dominant use of mercury in products in 2001 was in switches and wiring devices at 42 percent (103 metric tons), followed by measuring and control devices at 28 percent (69 metric tons), dental amalgam at 14 percent (34 metric tons), and electrical lighting at 9 percent (21 metric tons).

Mercury is also found in laboratories, including school science labs. Breakage or spillage of mercury supplies and mercury-containing lab equipment creates the potential for inhalation exposure to airborne mercury indoors. Mercury in schools can pose a significant exposure concern for children and adults.

In 2001, the largest use of mercury in manufacturing processes was by the chlor-alkali industry (producers of chlorine and caustic soda), estimated at 38 metric tons, or 12 percent of overall mercury use by U.S. industry.[94]

Progress to date. Over the past two decades there has been a dramatic drop in mercury use by industries in the United States, decreasing 83 percent between 1980 and 1997, from 2,225 metric tons to 381 metric tons (see Figure 4).[95] This reduction in use was due in large part to state and congressional limits placed on mercury use in batteries, EPA's regulatory ban on mercury in paint, closure of some mercury-cell chlor-alkali manufacturing plants, and progress made under the U.S./ Canada Great Lakes Binational Toxics Strategy, a voluntary agreement which set forth a goal of 50 percent reduction in the deliberate use of mercury nationwide by 2006.[96]

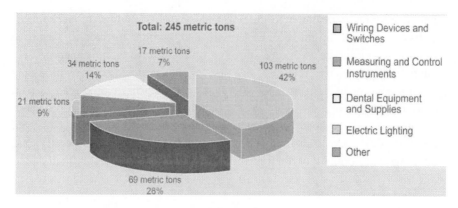

Figure 3. Total 2001 U.S. Mercury Use in Products.[93]

The lamp industry has made significant progress in reducing use of mercury. The National Electrical Manufacturers Association (NEMA) reported that its members have significantly reduced use of mercury in lamps while increasing their production of lamps. In 1990, NEMA estimates that its lamp members used 23.6 tons of mercury in slightly fewer than 500 million mercury-containing lamps. After a concerted effort to reduce mercury use, this mercury usage declined to 7 tons by 2003. In the same timeframe, sales by NEMA lamp members have increased to 650 million mercury-containing lamps. The Association of Mercury and Lamp Recyclers reports that lamp recycling has increased from fewer than 10 million lamps in 1990 to 156 million lamps in 2003.[97]

As a result of a voluntary commitment to mercury reduction made by the U.S. Chlorine Institute under the Great Lakes Binational Toxics Strategy, the chlor-alkali industry has made significant progress in reducing its mercury use since 1995. The U.S. Chlorine Institute's Ninth Annual Report to EPA showed a 91 percent reduction between 1995 and 2005 in mercury used in the U.S. production of chlorine and caustic soda, after adjusting for shut down facilities.[98]

EPA's Hospitals for a Healthy Environment (H2E) program is a partnership among EPA, the American Hospital Association (AHA), the American Nurses Association, and Health Care Without Harm to encourage hospitals to eliminate the use and purchase of mercury-containing products such as measurement and control devices.[99] Under H2E, these health care facilities have pledged to eliminate mercury use and waste whenever possible by 2005 and to reduce all types of waste by 2010.

State, Tribal, and Local Government Use Reduction Efforts

Many state, tribal, and local governments have been leaders in reducing mercury use. States have developed innovative mercury use and release reduction laws and regulations that supplement, and in some cases provide a model for, national efforts. For example, all of the New England states have adopted legislation to reduce mercury use in products.[100]

States, tribes, and local governments have played a key role in outreach to the business community and to the general public about the importance of properly disposing of mercury-containing products and about alternatives to such products. Many states and local governments have sponsored mercury collection/replacement programs for businesses and households for products such as mercury thermometers. They have also made special efforts to educate and encourage hospitals and schools to eliminate the use of mercury and mercury-containing products. For example, over the past few years, the northeast states, in conjunction with the eastern Canadian provinces, have collected over 2,000 pounds of mercury from cleanout efforts at over 200 schools.[101] These efforts have been key to the progress made to date on reducing mercury use in school science laboratories.

Likewise, several states such as Maine, Texas, and localities such as Alameda County, California have built green purchasing requirements that specify the use of non-mercury alternatives into their state procurement systems.

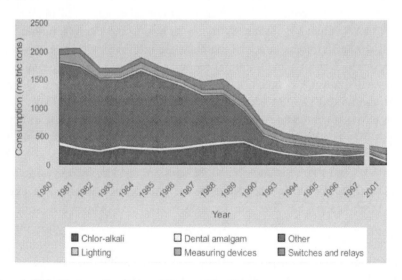

Figure 4. U.S. Mercury Product and Process Use Trends.

Future focus. During the next ten years, EPA will focus on uses that would lead to risk, where cost-effective substitutes exist; promote reducing mercury in processes and products where benefits of such reductions would justify the costs, even where cost-effective substitutes do not exist; and work to identify and encourage development of alternatives to essential uses of mercury that lead to risk by working with state and tribal partners, industry, and non-governmental organizations. The Agency's use reduction activities will be conducted in the context of the global market for commodity-grade elemental mercury and the need for global use reductions. (See Section III for further discussion of the mercury commodity market.) EPA will continue to support and build on successful state and local efforts by funding selected mercury projects, providing information about mercury sources and reduction opportunities, and coordinating joint efforts to further progress on addressing mercury use. EPA will also continue to work with other countries and international organizations to address global demand for and use of mercury as discussed further in Section V on international mercury sources.

Need for a National Mercury Use Database

Reliable and publicly available data on mercury use is a prerequisite to gauging the success of EPA initiatives to reduce the use of mercury. In 1998 the U.S. Geological Survey discontinued its annual reporting of mercury use, due to low voluntary response from mercury-using manufacturers. More recently, other limited sources of mercury use information have emerged: (1) the U.S. Chlorine Institute's annual report to EPA on mercury usage by the chlor-alkali industry;[102] and (2) the Northeast Waste Management Officials' Association's (NEWMOA) database on mercury-containing products, housed in NEWMOA's Interstate Mercury Education and Reduction Clearinghouse (IMERC).[103] The IMERC database contains annual data (beginning with 2001) required from manufacturers by the states of Connecticut, Maine, New Hampshire, and Rhode Island on national sales of specific mercury-containing products that are sold in these four states. The IMERC database is updated every three years. The base year for data is 2001; companies are required to report on 2004 data in 2005. EPA is evaluating how best to build upon this information as it is developing its database for mercury use in products and processes nationwide. A national use database will enable EPA and its partners to evaluate the effectiveness of its outreach activities.

Priority Activities for Reducing Mercury Uses

To further progress in reducing risks associated with mercury use, EPA will continue to pursue a number of priority activities. These activities are based on considerations of the quantity of mercury used by specific industry categories; opportunities to provide national leadership; and opportunities to work in partnership with industries, other federal agencies, state, tribal and local governments, other institutions, and public interest groups.

Industrial Processes

- *Track Reductions by Mercury-Cell Chlor-Alkali Facilities* – EPA will continue to monitor the use of mercury by the chlor-alkali industry through the EPA/U.S. Chlorine Institute voluntary agreement on use reporting for the remaining U.S. mercury-cell chlor-alkali plants. **Timeline: Ongoing through 2006**

Mercury-Containing Products

- *Further Reduce Risks Associated with Mercury Use Using TSCA Authorities and Voluntary Mechanisms* – EPA will focus its new reduction efforts on switches, relays, and measuring devices because these sectors represent the majority of mercury use in products, and cost-effective alternatives are available for many uses in these categories. EPA will conduct a preliminary market analysis of mercury switches, relays, and measurement devices to identify candidate product manufacturers to partner with the Agency to reduce mercury use. Building upon successful state regulatory programs, EPA will pursue further use reductions in this product area using TSCA and voluntary mechanisms. **Timeline: Proposed auto switch significant new use rule in 2006**
- *Develop Database to Track Reductions in Mercury Use by Key Sectors*– EPA is compiling and assessing information on mercury use and substitutes from existing data sources. The Agency will explore using various mechanisms to improve the comprehensiveness and reliability of its national database on mercury use, supply, and

substitutes. This information also will allow EPA to evaluate the effectiveness of its outreach activities on mercury-containing products. **Timeline: Data collection is ongoing; database in 2007**

- *Promote Procurement of Non-Mercury Products by Federal Agencies* – EPA is compiling a list of alternative non-mercury products with a special emphasis on those that contain non-mercury switches, relays, and measuring devices. EPA will compile and convey information—such as federal, state, and local bid specifications—to federal purchasers using its Environmentally Preferable Products (EPP) Database.[104] The intent is to harness the large federal buying power to increase demand for non-mercury products. EPA will also make such information available to other interested purchasers, including state, tribal, and local governments; large industrial purchasers currently using mercury switches and relays (such as manufacturers of cars, airplanes, and appliances); institutional purchasers such as hospitals and schools; and individual consumers. **Timeline: Ongoing**

- *Partner with Automobile Manufacturers to Eliminate Mercury* – EPA will work with the auto manufacturers on additional mercury use reduction and elimination of mercury from products, such as high-intensity discharge (HID) headlights. EPA will provide auto manufacturers with information on non-mercury alternatives to auto components through its Green Suppliers Network, an EPA partnership effort with manufacturers and their supply chains.[105] **Timeline: Enhance partnership efforts on auto products in 2006**

- *Reduce Mercury in Health Care Facilities* – EPA will continue partnerships with the American Hospital Association (AHA), the American Nurses Association, and Health Care Without Harm to encourage hospitals to eliminate the purchase of mercury-containing products such as measurement and control devices, and properly dispose of mercury-containing products currently in health care facilities. EPA will expand these efforts by recruiting additional facilities. **Timeline: Recruit 2,000 new facilities by 2007**

- *Promote Mercury Reduction in Schools* – Building upon the successful work of the mercury-in-schools projects throughout the country by states and EPA regions, EPA will continue to work with school administrators and policy makers to promote the substitution of mercury with environmentally preferable chemicals through procurement policy guidelines and the use of green chemistry; the removal of elemental mercury, mercury reagents, and mercury waste products from school laboratories; the replacement of mercury-containing devices with safer non-mercury-containing devices in all school facilities; and the use of software to educate school maintenance workers and decisionmakers about potential environmental hazards in schools and ways to reduce them. EPA is developing a handbook, "Chemical Management for Schools: Recommended Actions for Administrators," which will help schools safely manage chemicals, including mercury. This guidance will help school officials ensure the health and safety of the students and school employees. **Timeline: Finalize Chemicals Management Document in 2006**

- *Schools Chemical Cleanout Campaign (SC3)* – Existing stocks of outdated, unknown, excessive or unnecessarily hazardous chemicals—are present in schools across the country. These chemicals can pose safety and health risks to students and staff, and a number of widely reported incidents involving such chemicals have resulted in school closures and costly clean-ups. To reduce the number of these incidents, the Agency has initiated the Schools Chemical Cleanout Campaign (SC3)[106] which promotes removal of existing stocks of hazardous chemicals from secondary schools; safe chemical management; and national awareness. The ultimate goal of the SC3 is to create a chemically safer school environment in which chemicals are purchased wisely, stored safely, handled by trained personnel, used responsibly, and disposed of properly. In the summer of 2004, EPA launched ten SC3 pilots, one in each EPA region. EPA provided funding for an additional eight pilots in 2005. Outreach materials are now available on the website at www.epa.gov/sc3. **Timeline: Ongoing**

- *Promote Mercury Product Use Reduction Partnerships* – Many current mercury uses in products have cost-effective, mercury-free alternatives. EPA is currently inviting companies to voluntarily commit to mercury product use reduction and phase-out goals and to become partners in EPA's National Partnership for Environmental Priorities (NPEP) Program. As a component of these partnerships,

EPA is promoting mercury-containing product take-back/recycling programs and providing technical assistance to industry in achieving their NPEP goals. **Timeline: Ongoing**

- *Promote the Mercury Challenge* – EPA is currently inviting companies to commit to establish inventories of mercury; remove mercury and mercury-containing equipment from their plants; and institute purchasing policies to reduce mercury use. This mercury challenge is a component of the NPEP program.[107]

III. Managing Commodity-Grade Mercury Supplies

Overview

The Agency expects that an excess supply of elemental, commodity-grade mercury will emerge on the market over the coming years as various secondary sources of mercury—especially the expected phase-out of mercury-cell chlor-alkali plants—overtake a shrinking demand for mercury-containing products and industrial use of mercury. As a result, there will be an increasing need to safely manage mercury supplies for the long term. Ultimately, it will be important to look at ways to permanently "retire" most supplies of mercury that will eventually have little or no economic value. EPA estimates that current world demand for mercury is approximately 2,000 metric tons per year (mt/yr). Although highly variable from one year to the next, the amount of mercury available in commerce globally is also estimated at 2,000 mt/yr.[108] Other estimates prepared for the European Union (EU) indicate that the global mercury supply may be over 3,300 metric tons.[109] It is important to note that supply and demand numbers for countries outside the U.S. and Europe are very rough estimates. In the absence of efforts to retire mercury supplies, there is a danger that supplied mercury will find uses that have already been banned or eliminated in some countries, particularly in the developing world, possibly leading to unnecessary releases.

Sources. In recent years, approximately one-half of the world mercury supply has come from mercury mines in Spain, Algeria, and Kyrgyzstan (although Spain is no longer mining mercury). China has also mined mercury to meet its domestic demand.[110] There have been no active mercury mines in the U.S. since 1990. The remaining half of the world's mercury supply comes from secondary sources, such as industrial wastes and scrap products, as byproduct from gold mines in the U.S. and abroad, and from closing mercury-cell chlor-alkali plants. The secondary mercury produced from these other sources is price-insensitive because the mercury results from environmental regulations and polices that require or encourage recovery (e.g., RCRA land disposal restrictions), and from industrial process conversions to non-mercury processes. Environmental regulations and polices that require mercury recovery can override the market's natural tendency over the long term to match supply with demand. Whereas the long-term trend for mercury mining has been one of decline, secondary production has remained relatively constant. It may even increase as mercury continues to be recycled/recovered and more mercury-cell chlor-alkali plants close, thereby making more mercury available to the secondary market.

The most significant factor driving the timing of a global mercury surplus is the rate at which remaining U.S. and international mercury-cell chlor-alkali plants close and liquidate their stocks of some 22,000 metric tons. Of these stocks, mercury-cell chlor-alkali plants in the U.S. account for about 2,600 metric tons of mercury stocks.[111] Mercury-cell chlor-alkali plants are being closed at the end of their useful life in the U.S. and abroad due to the industry's conversion to non-mercury technologies, a shrinking customer base, and high energy costs.

Progress to date. The Department of Defense (DoD) has mercury stocks that are being stored. The DoD has 4,436 metric tons of mercury in its strategic stockpile. DoD has sold some of its mercury stocks in the past, but since 1994 DoD has been storing its mercury in response to requests from EPA, states, and non-governmental organizations (NGOs). On April 30, 2004, the Defense National Stockpile Center (DNSC) published its final Mercury Management Environmental Impact Statement regarding the disposition of its mercury.[112] The DNSC decided to store its mercury at one location for at least a 40-year period. In addition, the Department of Energy has a known supply of 1,306 tons of mercury.

State and local governments have promoted public and private collection programs for both bulk elemental mercury and discarded mercury-containing products. Some businesses are also collecting unwanted mercury or mercury-containing products (e.g., thermostats). The total amount of mercury collected through these programs is unclear. Most of this mercury is sent to retorters, and it is likely that the supply of mercury will increase due to successful collection programs and efforts to eliminate mercury from schools, laboratories, and businesses.

The Environmental Council of the States (ECOS) and the Quicksilver Caucus (QSC), a coalition of state associations concerned with mercury pollution, have indicated that states do not have the resources or desire to manage surplus mercury for the long term and are looking to the federal government to address this issue.[113] Environmental groups and the U.S. Chlorine Institute are also looking to the federal government to address or assume responsibility for all private sector commodity-grade mercury that exceeds U.S. demand.

In addition, EPA's Office of Research and Development conducted research and published a report in 2005 on the technical and economic feasibility of selected land disposal technologies in a monofill context, as compared to above-ground storage for elemental mercury.[114]

Future focus. The issue of whether the federal government, states, or the private sector should take responsibility for managing commodity-grade mercury supplies from state and private sources is an important policy decision. Decisions regarding the disposition of commodity-grade mercury should be made in light of the global mercury market; data and research needs; public policy, statutory, and economic considerations; and the views of Congress, states, tribes, and nongovernmental organizations.

Ultimately, it will be important to look at ways to permanently "retire" non-federally owned or managed commodity-grade mercury that will eventually have little or even negative economic value. Disposal of commodity-grade mercury would require regulatory changes, as current regulations under the Resource Conservation and Recovery Act (RCRA) require high concentration mercury wastes to be retorted for mercury recovery and reuse.[115]

Additional information on mercury supplies and flows would allow for more informed policy choices and decisions on this issue, and to better estimate when the global mercury surplus may occur. EPA, states, tribes, and the private sector must continue efforts, domestically and internationally, to address exposure, potential reduction strategies, and the quantity of mercury that will ultimately need to be stored or land disposed permanently.

Priority Activities for Addressing Mercury Supplies

Address Data Gaps on Mercury Supplies

- *Publish Initial Report and Assemble Existing Data on Domestic and Global Commodity Mercury Production and Use* – EPA will explore with industry and other federal agencies ways to fill information gaps on annual production and use of commodity mercury. **Timeline: 2006**

Safe Storage Practices for Disposal of Mercury

- *Establish a Process to Address Mercury Surplus Issues* – In 2006, EPA will work with other agencies to initiate a process with technical experts and interested parties to discuss options for addressing the expected mercury surplus over the next 10–30 years, and how to encourage the phase-out of mercury mining abroad. **Timeline: Initiate discussion in 2006**

IV. COMMUNICATING TO THE PUBLIC ABOUT MERCURY EXPOSURE RISKS

Overview

While the Agency is pursuing regulatory and voluntary activities aimed at industrial reduction of mercury releases and uses, EPA will also increase its risk communication and outreach activities to help people avoid or reduce their exposure to mercury in the near term. The most common way people in the U.S. are exposed to mercury is by eating fish containing methylmercury (an organic mercury compound). Consumption of fish with higher methylmercury levels can lead to elevated levels of methylmercury in the bloodstream of unborn babies and young children and may harm their developing nervous system.[116] The primary tool for reaching and educating affected populations has been through fish consumption advisories issued by states, tribes, and FDA. For example, in March 2004, EPA and FDA issued a joint federal fish consumption advisory for mercury in fish and shellfish that helps consumers understand the benefits of fish consumption, the risks of consumption to certain sub-populations (e.g., groups with routinely high consumption), and mercury levels in certain fish.

WHAT YOU NEED TO KNOW ABOUT MERCURY IN FISH AND SHELLFISH

U.S. Food and Drug Administration and U.S. Environmental Protection Agency Advice for
Women Who Might Become Pregnant, Women Who Are Pregnant, Nursing Mothers, and Young Children

1. Do not eat:
   - Shark
   - Swordfish
   - King Mackerel
   - Tilefish

   They contain high levels of mercury.
2. Eat up to 12 ounces (2 average meals) a week of a variety of fish and shellfish that are lower in mercury.
   - Five of the most commonly eaten fish that are low in mercury are shrimp, canned light tuna, salmon, pollock, and catfish.
   - Another commonly eaten fish, albacore ("white") tuna has more mercury than canned light tuna. So, when choosing your two meals of fish and shellfish, you may eat up to 6 ounces (one average meal) of albacore tuna per week.
3. Check local advisories about the safety of fish caught by family and friends in your local lakes, rivers and coastal areas.

If no advice is available, eat up to 6 ounces (one average meal) per week of fish you catch from local waters, but don't consume any other fish during that week. Follow these same recommendations when feeding fish and shellfish to your young child, but serve smaller portions.

For more information, please visit: www.epa.gov/waterscience/ fishadvice/advice.html

---

Fish and shellfish are an important part of a healthy diet, since they contain high quality protein and other essential nutrients, are low in saturated fat, and contain omega-3 fatty acids. A well-balanced diet that includes a variety of fish and shellfish can contribute to heart health and children's proper growth and development. Research shows that most people's fish consumption does not cause a health concern.

EPA and FDA have issued fish consumption advice to help consumers understand the connection between the benefits of fish and possible risks of methylmercury exposure. Elevated methylmercury in the blood stream of unborn babies and young children may harm the nervous system, impairing the child's ability to learn and process information. Certain sub-populations may be at higher risk than the general population because of their routinely high consumption of fish and shellfish (e.g., tribal and other subsistence fishers and their families who rely heavily on locally caught fish for the majority of their diet).

Although people are exposed to methylmercury via the dietary route, there are also some non-dietary sources of mercury exposure. Many consumers are not aware that mercury has been used for years in common household products such as thermostats. Releases from the manufacture of mercury-containing products and inappropriate disposal of these products have contributed to mercury entering the environment and ultimately the food chain. Misuse of or accidental breakage of some products can create indoor air health risks and expose consumers to dangerous levels of mercury. In addition, certain cultural or religious uses of mercury may also result in harmful mercury exposure. The number of individuals exposed in the U.S. in this way is very small.

The Agency will make it a priority to provide consumers with reliable risk information about mercury exposure so that they can make informed choices about the fish they eat and the products they use.

Progress to date. EPA has directed most of its mercury risk communication activities toward raising awareness about dietary practices. The FDA-EPA national advisory, *What You Need to Know About Mercury in Fish and Shellfish*, provides advice for women who might become pregnant; women who are pregnant; nursing mothers; and young children.[117] This advisory represents the first time FDA and EPA have combined their advice into a single uniform advisory. During the summer and fall of 2004, the two agencies distributed brochures about the advisory to approximately 200,000 medical providers in the U.S.

In September 2005, EPA sponsored the Eighth Annual National Forum on Contaminants in Fish ("Fish Forum"). The forum provided an opportunity for people who have an interest in the subject of advisories, from both the public and private sectors, to discuss scientific and policy issues, risks and benefits, and communication strategies associated with exposure to chemical contaminants in sport-and subsistence-caught fish and shellfish. In September 2005, the 13th straight year, EPA released its National Listing of Fish Advisories, a summary of information on locally-issued fish advisories and safe-eating guidelines.[118] This information is provided to EPA annually by states, territories, and tribes.

States and tribes issue fish consumption advisories if elevated concentrations of chemicals such as mercury are found in local fish. States monitor their waters by sampling fish tissue for persistent pollutants that bioaccumulate. States issue their advisories and guidelines voluntarily and have flexibility in what criteria they use and how the data are collected. As a result, there are significant variations in the number of waters tested, the pollutants tested for, and the threshold for issuing advisories. Based on self-reporting, the national trend is for states to monitor different waters each year, generally without retesting waters monitored in previous years.[119] As new waters are tested and results are added to previous years' findings, the number of fish advisories continues to rise. EPA makes information on the fish advisories, as well as Fish Forum proceedings, easily accessible to the public on its website.

Although most of EPA's risk communication efforts have been directed to increasing awareness of mercury in the food chain, the Agency has also investigated non-dietary sources of mercury exposure about which the public should be aware. Risk communication has been conducted in conjunction with mercury reduction activities, such as school clean-outs or thermometer collection programs. In many cases, critical mercury outreach to schools and communities would not otherwise occur without EPA assistance. For example, EPA's Region 6 has identified a particular need for such support in communities on the U.S./Mexico border.

EPA's national efforts on mercury risk communication have been aimed at making information widely available to the public and at co-sponsoring national conferences that bring together people from across the country to share information on mercury risk communication. A unique exposure concern is raised by ritualistic use of mercury in certain cultural communities. For this reason, in January 1999, EPA and the U.S. Agency for Toxic Substances and Disease Registry (ATSDR) convened the Task Force on Ritualistic Uses of Mercury to recommend an appropriate course of action regarding the use of elemental mercury as part of certain folk practices and religious traditions. The Task Force prepared a report in 2002 which recommended approaches that rely primarily on community outreach and education activities to inform mercury suppliers and the public about mercury's risks, and encourage the use of safer alternatives.[120]

In January 2005, EPA launched its consolidated website on mercury, www.epa.gov/mercury.[121] This new website, organized by subject matter and geographic region, provides one location to find information about mercury in a useful format for the American public. Because the most effective mercury risk communication activities will be carried out at the state and local level, another important contribution to mercury risk communication is the provision of grants, cooperative agreements, and other types of funding for state, tribal, and local mercury risk communication activities.

States, tribes, and local governments have also conducted outreach activities in conjunction with most of the mercury collection programs mentioned in Sections I and II on addressing mercury releases and uses in processes and products. In order to get a high rate of participation in these voluntary programs, it is important to educate the public on the risks of mercury exposure, the need for proper disposal of mercury-containing products, and the availability of safe, non-mercury alternatives. For example, in an innovative project, the state of Minnesota trained a dog to locate mercury in buildings by sense of smell. Minnesota's Mercury-Free Zone Program is modeled after a Swedish program that uses dogs to detect mercury in schools.[122] Schools that take the mercury-free pledge are eligible to receive a visit from Clancy the mercury dog. Clancy has received media coverage which has raised general awareness of the dangers of mercury and the need to dispose of mercury responsibly. States, tribes, and local governments are in the best position to develop material tailored to local populations. For example, the state of Washington is using an EPA grant to conduct a survey of fish consumption among Asian/Pacific Islander populations in the Puget Sound region. As part of this project, the state will identify community groups to educate these populations in a culturally sensitive manner by tailoring messages and translating documents.

Future focus. As long as mercury is present in the environment and in food and consumer products, consumers will need reliable risk information about mercury exposure; about making informed choices regarding the benefits of fish consumption, the risks of consumption for certain groups, and mercury levels in certain fish; and about the purchase, use, and disposal of mercury-containing products and mercury-free alternatives. EPA will continue to provide support for national and local outreach and education programs on the effects of mercury and consumer choices. EPA will also support risk communication and outreach efforts about mercury through its international activities and programs.

Priority Activities for Mercury Risk Communication

- ***Continue Assistance in Implementing Fish Advisories*** – EPA will continue to work closely with FDA to implement the 2004 joint EPA-FDA national fish advisory for methylmercury across the U.S. EPA will also work with FDA to continue targeted outreach efforts to the U.S. medical community to provide information on dietary risks of methylmercury exposure, and ways that medical professionals can help patients and their families reduce exposure to mercury while maintaining a healthy diet. EPA will continue to assist the states and tribes with development and communication of their fish advisories through the National Forum on Contaminants in Fish (held every 15–18 months), updating of risk communication guidance documents, and updating the National Listing of Advisories. **Timeline: Ongoing; Biennial Fish Forums**

- ***Maintain Centralized Mercury Portal Website*** – EPA will provide up-to-date information on all aspects of the risk of mercury exposure through food consumption and product use by maintaining its electronic Mercury Portal Website, which will be EPA's primary mechanism for communicating with the public about mercury. **Timeline: Ongoing**

- ***Assist State, Tribal, and Local Government Mercury Outreach Activities*** – EPA will continue to assist and support state, tribal, and local government efforts to conduct mercury risk communication and outreach, research and mitigation activities addressing important routes of mercury exposure, and actions that can be taken by individual consumers to reduce mercury exposure and pollution. **Timeline: Ongoing**

- ***Outreach Activities to Consumers on Mercury-containing Products and Mercury-free Substitutes for Use in the Home*** – Building upon the information already available from states and other groups about consumer products that contain mercury, EPA will develop an inventory of mercury-containing products and mercury-free substitutes. EPA will also identify information gaps. EPA will make the information available on its website. **Timeline: 2006**

- *Outreach to Health Professionals and Health Care Associations* – Health professionals are an important partner in the dissemination of mercury risk information. EPA is working to educate health professionals about a variety of children's environmental health issues, including mercury. For example, EPA is coordinating an interagency effort to work with the Pediatric Environmental Health Specialty Units to provide pediatric consultative services covering mercury and other key concerns for children's environmental health. EPA will also partner with health care associations and universities to disseminate mercury risk information and increase proper mercury disposal in health care facilities. Through the Hospitals for a Healthy Environment (H2E) program, EPA and its regions will continue to work with universities to educate future health professionals in proper disposal of chemicals in hospitals. **Timeline: Ongoing**
- *Outreach to Schools on the Need to Remove Mercury* – As part of its national project to work with science teachers, curriculum developers, facilities managers, and pollution prevention professionals to promote mercury reduction in schools, EPA will work to make school officials and staff aware of the risks of exposure to mercury and the availability of mercury-free alternatives. This includes the use of software to educate school decisionmakers about potential environmental hazards in schools and ways to reduce them. **Timeline: Ongoing**
- *Conduct Public Awareness Evaluation for Dietary Issues* – To better educate the U.S. public on how to make informed dietary choices, FDA, with assistance from EPA, is conducting surveys to evaluate how well the U.S. public understands the effects of methylmercury exposure from eating certain fish and shellfish. **Timeline: Surveys conducted and completed during 2006/2007**

V. ADDRESSING INTERNATIONAL MERCURY SOURCES

Overview

EPA is actively engaged and collaborating with international organizations and partners to address risks associated with mercury uses, releases, and exposure. As previously discussed, the greatest mercury exposure to the general population is general population is from eating fish containing methyl-mercury, including marine fish. EPA has estimated that over three quarters (83 percent) of the mercury deposited in the U.S. originates from international sources (with the remaining 17 percent coming from U.S. and Canadian sources). These figures include mercury from natural and re-emitted sources. This estimate is based on an advanced, state-of-the-science modeling assessment of atmospheric fate, transport, and deposition of mercury. EPA's modeling indicates that a substantial variation in mercury deposition occurs across the U.S., with domestic sources influencing mercury deposition much more in the eastern U.S. and global sources being a more significant contributor to mercury deposition in the west, where relatively few domestic sources exist. The scientific community's understanding of mercury atmospheric chemistry is evolving, and there remain uncertainties regarding simulation of mercury in atmospheric chemistry models. EPA continues to work to advance the state of the science on mercury chemistry and fate and transport modeling.[124] International collaboration is critical to refining our understanding of global mercury sources, international transport pathways, and environmental impacts, and most importantly, for addressing the adverse impacts of mercury on human health and the environment globally.

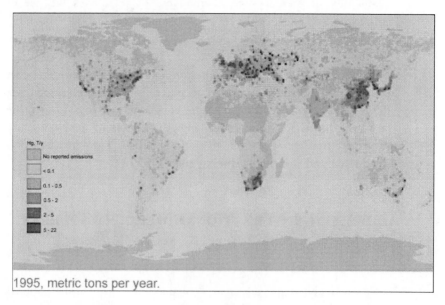

Figure 5. Where are Man-Made Mercury Emissions Originating?[123]

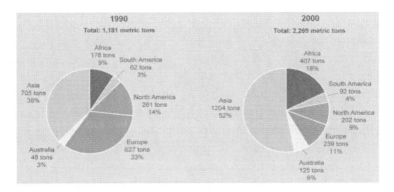

Figure 6. Man-Made Air Emissions of Mercury: Distribution by Region in 1990 and 2000.[125]

Sources. A number of key international emission sources contribute to global cycling and deposition of mercury via air pathways, including: coal-fired combustion sources; mining and metals production, such as smelting; mercury-cell chlor-alkali manufacturing facilities; and combustion or incineration of waste products containing mercury. The United Nations Environment Program (UNEP) estimates that the total global emissions of mercury (anthropogenic and natural to the atmosphere) range from 4,400 to 7,500 metric tons per year.[126] EPA estimates that 50–70 percent of current global anthropogenic atmospheric emissions come from fuel combustion, and much of this is from China, India, and other Asian countries.[127] Coal consumption in Asia is expected to grow significantly over the next 20 years. This source of mercury emissions may grow substantially if left unaddressed.[128] Small-scale "artisanal" gold and silver mining is an important mercury emissions source in numerous Asian, South American, and African countries. Atmospheric mercury emissions from artisanal gold mining have been estimated by UNEP to be about 300 metric tons per year,[129] but some experts estimate that total mercury releases from artisanal gold mining are between 650 and 1,000 metric tons per year on a global basis.[130] An estimated 13 million people in 55 countries work and are affected by occupational exposures in artisanal mining.[131]

Using data presented in the 2002 United Nations Environment Program Global Mercury Assessment, EPA has calculated that mercury-cell chlor-alkali factories are the third largest source of atmospheric mercury releases to the global environment. While the number of mercury-cell chlor-alkali facilities has been greatly reduced in the United States and Europe over the last two decades, the process is prevalent in many parts of the world including Russia, several South American countries, and India, which is estimated to have the most plants of any developing country.[132] EPA estimates that there may be 135–170 mercury-cell plants globally, with half located in developing countries.[133]

Global estimates for mercury use in processes and products range from 2,000– 3,400 metric tons per year.[134] Mercury-cell chlor-alkali facilities are among the principal users of mercury in the world. In addition to industrial uses, mercury has been used in numerous products, including household appliances, electronics, batteries, automobile switches, dental amalgam, and thermometers. While mercury use in pesticides, fungicides, paints, and most batteries has been banned or phased-out in the U.S. and other developed countries, these uses are continuing in developing countries. For example, battery production accounts for an estimated one third of global mercury use in products (see Figure 7).[135]

Progress to date. EPA is currently engaged in the implementation of a wide range of bilateral, regional, and international programs and agreements to address mercury uses, releases, and the resulting exposure around the globe. These include:

- *U.S./Canada Great Lakes Binational Toxics Strategy,* which provides a framework for actions to reduce or eliminate mercury and other persistent toxic substances. The Strategy sets forth challenge goals to reduce mercury use by 50 percent and to reduce releases by 50 percent by 2006 (from the 1990 baseline). The use goal has been met. The releases goal has almost been met. Mercury releases have decreased by 47 percent. By 2006, additional regulations and voluntary activities are expected to reduce mercury emissions by at least 50 percent, meeting the release goal as well.[136]
- *New England Governors/Eastern Canadian Premiers Regional Mercury Action Plan,* which establishes long-term and short-term regional mercury reduction goals. The plan addresses mercury emission reductions; source reduction and safe waste management; outreach and education; and research, analysis and strategic monitoring. Due to successfully reaching the goal of 50 percent reduction of emissions by 2003, the Governors and Premiers are now working on meeting a 75 percent reduction goal for emissions by 2010.[137]

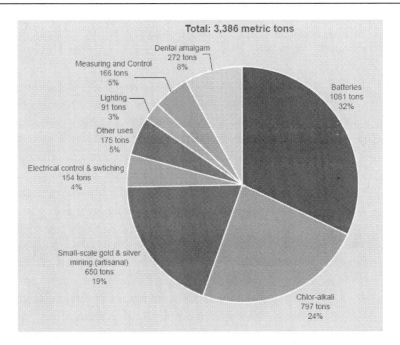

Figure 7. Global Mercury Use, 2000.

- *Commission for Environmental Cooperation (CEC) North American Regional Action Plan for Mercury,* which aims to reduce man-made mercury releases to the North American environment through appropriate international and national initiatives to amounts that are attributable to naturally-occurring levels and fluxes. The U.S. has made considerable progress in implementing the provisions of the plan regarding mercury air emissions; processes, operations, and products; and waste management; as well as research, monitoring, modeling, and inventories; and communication activities.[138]

- *United Nations Economic Commission for Europe (UNECE) Convention on Long-range Transboundary Air Pollution Protocol on Heavy Metals* is a legally-binding agreement that targets emissions of cadmium, lead, and mercury. The U.S. is a party to the Heavy Metals Protocol, which went into effect in December 2003. The protocol aims to cut emissions from industrial sources, combustion processes, and waste incineration through application of best available technologies and emission limit values for new and existing stationary sources. The protocol also requires mandatory mercury concentration limits for certain types of batteries, and encourages parties to consider various management measures to address use of mercury in other products. The U.S. meets the provisions of the Heavy Metals Protocol.[139]

- **UNEP Mercury Program,** which was created at the February 2003 meeting of the United Nations Environment Program (UNEP) Governing Council. The United States government was instrumental in providing much of the initial funding and leadership for the creation of the UNEP Mercury Program. This program is based on the key finding of the *2002 UNEP Global Mercury Assessment* that there is sufficient evidence of significant global adverse impacts from mercury and its compounds to warrant international action to reduce the risks to human health and the environment. Supported by the 130 nations attending the Governing Council meeting, the UNEP Mercury Program endorses immediate actions to reduce mercury uses and releases, assist developing countries to create mercury emissions inventories, raise awareness, and provide technical assistance. The U.S. government has been involved in all of these efforts, and has funded the majority of the UNEP Mercury Program to date. EPA funded technical staff to work in the UNEP Mercury Program for two years, provided technical review of UNEP draft mercury guidance, and sent experts to conduct training at the UNEP regional mercury workshops.[140]

At the twenty-third session of the UNEP Governing Council, which was held in Nairobi, Kenya, February 21– 25, 2005, delegates agreed to further develop the UNEP Mercury Program and to support the efforts of countries to take action to reduce mercury exposure, releases, and uses. The Governing Council urged governments, intergovernmental and nongovernmental organizations, and the private sector to develop and implement partnerships in a clear, transparent, and accountable manner to reduce the risks of mercury to human health and the environment.[141]

The U.S. initiated five mercury partnerships for: (1) artisanal and small-scale gold mining; (2) chlor-alkali manufacturing; (3) products; (4) coal combustion; and (5) fate and transport research. EPA held consultative meetings with other countries and domestic and international stakeholders on the first three partnerships in 2005. The partnerships created will leverage resources, technical expertise, technology transfer, and information exchanges to provide immediate, effective action that will result in tangible reductions of mercury use and emissions.[142]

- **United Nations Industrial Development Organization (UNIDO) Global Mercury Project,** which provides training on best management practices to reduce occupational exposures, to reduce emissions, and to reduce the amount of mercury used in small-scale "artisanal" gold and silver mining operations around the world. EPA has provided funding and technical expertise to assist in this effort.[143]

- **Arctic Mercury Project,** which was developed in the context of the Arctic Council Action Plan (ACAP) and the Arctic Monitoring and Assessment Program (AMAP). EPA has worked to strengthen capacity building and technical cooperation programs among the Arctic countries, particularly to assist Russia in the development of Russia's mercury action plan.[144] In 2005, two ACAP mercury reports were issued. The first, an "Arctic Mercury Releases Inventory," summarizes current releases, usage, and disposal of mercury within all eight Arctic countries. The second, an "Assessment of Mercury Releases from the Russian Federation," represents the first comprehensive assessment of mercury releases at the national level by that country. With the cooperation of the Russian authorities, a limited number of point sources in the Russian Federation are being evaluated in terms of their potential as sites for mercury demonstration projects. The Agency is coordinating U.S. federal government involvement, which includes the U.S. Geological Survey, Department of Energy, Department of State, and National Oceanic and Atmospheric Administration.

Future focus. EPA will continue to work with the U.S. Department of State and other federal agencies to provide international leadership in addressing mercury in international fora, including the CEC, UNECE, Arctic Council, and UNEP. Consistent with the 2005 UNEP Governing Council Decision on mercury, the goal of the U.S. government is to reduce human and ecosystem risks associated with the use and emissions of mercury from international sources. Global mercury reductions can be accomplished by addressing all major aspects of the global mercury problem and collaborating on the development of partnerships and specific results-oriented projects to reduce mercury uses and emissions nationally, regionally, and globally. It is critical to more fully engage developed and developing countries, industry, environmental groups, international organizations, and funding institutions to bring needed technical expertise and financial resources to address the global mercury problem.

Priority Activities to Reduce Global Mercury Sources and Releases

The following is a list of important components to an international approach to facilitate global reductions in mercury use, releases, and exposure, followed by brief descriptions, and EPA's priority actions in each area. These activities build upon and complement existing actions under UNEP, UNECE, Arctic Council, UNIDO, and multi-lateral and bilateral agreements, and may include the development of or participation in specific partnerships and projects in the following areas:

- Increase international awareness of mercury risks and risk communication approaches
- Improve global understanding of international emissions sources, releases and transport mechanisms
- Address mercury emissions from point sources
- Address mercury use in products and processes where there is an opportunity to reduce risk
- Address mercury supply issues
- Improve management of mercury-containing wastes and surplus mercury
- ***Increase International Awareness of Mercury Risks and Risk Communication Approaches*** – There is a need to enhance international awareness and understanding of mercury sources (national, regional, and global) and risks to the general public. It is important to develop and share key health messages and methods regarding exposure from dietary sources (e.g., fish consumption advisories, testing methods, and protocols for determining the level of mercury in fish) and non-dietary sources (e.g., consumer products) and the need to use mercury alternatives.
  EPA will work with its federal, state, nongovernmental, and international partners to:
  - Share sampling and analysis protocols that have been developed to determine the level of mercury in fish. **Timeline: Ongoing**
  - Support international outreach efforts to communicate risk. **Timeline: Ongoing**
- ***Improve International Understanding of Global Emissions Sources, Releases, and Transport Mechanisms*** – International cooperation has

helped shape understanding of mercury cycling on local, regional, and global scales, and determine the effects of mercury exposure on human health. Working with international partners is critical to improving understanding of mercury's global impacts. Areas of collaboration will include transport and fate research; development of production, use, source, and emissions data.

EPA will work with its federal, state, nongovernmental, and international partners to:

- Coordinate monitoring research and measurement work in Asia and elsewhere. **Timeline: Ongoing**
- Continue to conduct high altitude research in the U.S. to continue to transect with ongoing long-range transport monitoring in other parts of the world by the U.S. and other countries. **Timeline: Ongoing**
- Develop and implement workplans with UNEP, United Nations Institute for Training and Research (UNITAR) and other countries for assessment/inventory of mercury emissions and use. **Timeline: 2006**
- Support the development of a global partnership on mercury fate and transport research. **Timeline: Initiate in 2006**
- *Address Mercury Emissions from Point Sources* – Mercury is emitted to the air from combustion of fossil fuels, metal production, mining, mercury-cell chlor-alkali plants, waste incinerators, zinc smelters, and other point sources. International efforts to build on a number of existing techniques to reduce mercury emissions from these point sources by sharing information and expertise on air control technologies and multi-pollutant approaches will be key.

EPA will work with other federal agencies and departments to:

- Build on bilateral agreements to improve inventories and introduce control technologies in China, India, and Russia. **Timeline: Ongoing**
- Achieve reductions of global mercury emissions from the coalfired power sector through voluntary partnerships. **Timeline: Initiate in 2006**
- Raise awareness and knowledge of the applicability, effectiveness and cost of newly emerging mercury and multi-pollutant control technologies. **Timeline: Ongoing**
- Coordinate with the Chinese government, the private sector, Japan, and Canada to follow up on the workshop conducted in

Beijing, China in November 2005 to provide information on coalfired power plant multi-pollutant strategies and mercury control techniques, and to establish mechanisms to ensure continued information exchange with China and other countries. **Timeline: Ongoing**

- Review data on emissions from international large-scale metals mining operations in areas with high mercury content ore and explore options for transfer of EPA Region 9's Mining Voluntary Partnership Program. **Timeline: 2006/2007**

- *Address Mercury Use in Products and Processes* – Mercury is used globally in a variety of products and industrial processes. For most products and processes, there are cost-effective alternatives available that could replace mercury, which would reduce demand and emissions. There is a need for several sector-oriented approaches, including: (1) developing an industry partnership on chlor-alkali best management practices to reduce mercury use and emissions in countries or regions that use or emit the largest amounts of mercury; (2) reducing global demand for commodity-grade mercury through the use of inventories and partnering with national and international stakeholders to share information and approaches for mercury reductions and substitutes, particularly for measuring devices, batteries, and products used in the health care sector; and (3) promoting artisanal mining techniques that are safer and that eliminate or reduce the input of mercury.

  EPA will work with its federal, state, nongovernmental, industry, and international partners to:
  - Develop a multi-stakeholder global partnership on mercury-cell chloralkali sector. The partnership would include pilot projects; information exchange on best management practices and conversion to non-mercury processes; and use reporting, to reduce mercury releases from facilities that use or emit the largest amounts of mercury, including facilities in Mexico, India and Russia. **Timeline: Initiated in 2005**
  - Develop a multi-stakeholder global partnership for reducing or eliminating mercury use in products where there are cost-effective substitutes through pilot projects and activities, such as:
  - Sharing information and approaches for mercury reductions and substitutes (e.g., batteries and other products).

- Conducting a mercury product workshop to build capacity in Mexico and other countries in the Caribbean, Central and South America through the CEC Mercury Task Force (U.S., Canada, and Mexico) in Merida, Yucatan, Mexico in 2006.
- Developing country-specific use inventories, e.g. the Americas, Africa.
- Transferring successful reduction programs, such as EPA's successful Hospitals for a Healthy Environment program and the U.S. Green Suppliers Network to other countries, e.g., China. **Timeline: Initiate in 2006**
- Expand upon the UNIDO work on best management practices for artisanal mining to develop a multi-stakeholder global partnership on artisanal and small-scale gold mining to address use, exposure, and releases from this sector. Activities include the development of pilot projects, training, and monitoring, among others. **Timeline: Initiated in 2005**

- *Address Mercury Supply Issues* – Given declining demand in many developed countries, ongoing primary mercury mining, and growing global supplies from secondary sources, prices for mercury are expected to decline. A global mercury market surplus is expected by 2020 (but may occur earlier), keeping the price of mercury low and potentially discouraging its safe storage and management, the implementation of best management practices, substitution, and phase-out. The 2005 Governing Council Decision 23/9 requests that the UNEP prepare a report on mercury supply, trade, and demand information for consideration of possible further action. The Decision also requests governments, the private sector, and international organizations to take actions to reduce risks posed on a global scale by mercury in products and processes, such as considering curbing primary mercury production (mining) and introduction of mercury into commerce.

 EPA will work with the U.S. Department of State, other federal agencies, and international partners to:
- Share U.S. data on mercury imports and exports with UNEP. **Timeline: 2006**
- Explore mechanisms for facilitating the phase-out of primary mercury mining. **Timeline: Initiate in 2007**
- *Improve Management of Mercury-Containing Wastes and Surplus Mercury* – Mercury-containing wastes present significant challenges,

where municipal, hazardous, and medical waste management systems are ill-equipped to separate mercury from the waste stream. In addition, the global supply of commodity-grade mercury will increase as various secondary sources of mercury overtake the shrinking demand. There will be an increasing need to safely manage mercury supplies for the long term. Actions may include: (1) sharing information on successful approaches and best management practices for storage of commodity-grade mercury and safe treatment, retorting, and disposal of waste, including discarded mercury-containing products; (2) coordinating waste management activities with the Basel Convention's capacity-building program for waste management to avoid duplication and to leverage resources;[145] and (3) as technologies come on-line, building capacity to create waste disposal/ recycling programs for mercury-containing batteries, lamps, scrap metal, etc.

EPA will work with its federal and state partners, non-governmental organizations, and international partners to:

- Share U.S. best management practices for automobile switch removal, collection, and recycling programs. **Timeline: 2006**
- As previously discussed in the Commodity section of the Roadmap, EPA will establish a stakeholder process to address the mercury surplus issue. **Timeline: Initiate in 2006**

VI. CONDUCTING MERCURY RESEARCH AND MONITORING

Mercury Research Overview

There is much mercury research underway to investigate the occurrence and impact of mercury in the environment. EPA is actively engaged in a variety of research activities. In 2000, EPA's Office of Research and Development (ORD) published its *Mercury Research Strategy*,[146] which provides broad strategic directions for EPA's mercury research program.

The overarching goal of the research strategy is to provide information and data that reduce scientific uncertainties limiting the Agency's ability to assess and manage mercury and methylmercury risks. The strategy provides a rationale and framework for setting future mercury research priorities, which are reflected in EPA's Mercury Research Multi-Year Plan (MYP) covering the period 2002–2010.[147] This implementation plan contains longterm goals to: (1) reduce and prevent release of mercury into the environment; and (2) understand the transport and fate of mercury from release to the receptor and its effects on the receptor.

In conducting its mercury research program, ORD's in-house efforts are coupled with those of its Science to Achieve Results (STAR) Grants Program,[148] which sponsors extramural research on many topics by academic institutions and other not-for-profit entities. In addition, some of EPA's research is undertaken in cooperation with other organizations such as the U.S. Department of Energy (DOE) and the U.S. Geological Survey (USGS). Important coordination occurs among federal agencies and state, tribal, and local governments, through science forums such as the EPA/USGS Mercury Roundtable.[149] It is also important to note that additional mercury research activities are conducted by EPA headquarters and regional offices that are not described in ORD's Mercury Multi-Year Plan.

The primary exposure route addressed in the ORD Mercury Research Strategy involves fish consumption where deposited mercury is converted to methylmercury in water bodies, consumed by fish, and then accumulated in mammals, including humans that eat fish. Within the context of this primary exposure route, EPA has analyzed various scientific questions, including the following.

Key Scientific Questions

- How much methylmercury in fish consumed by the U.S. population is contributed by U.S. emissions relative to other sources of mercury (such as natural sources, emissions from sources in other countries, and re-emissions from the global pool)? How much, and over what time period, will levels of methylmercury in fish in the U.S. decrease due to reductions in environmental releases from U.S. sources?
- How much can mercury emissions from coal-fired power plant boilers and other combustion systems be reduced with innovative mercury-specific and multi-pollutant control technologies? What is the relative performance and cost of these approaches compared to currently available technologies?[150]
- What is the magnitude of contributions of mercury releases from noncombustion sources? How can the most significant releases be minimized?[151]

- What critical changes in human health are associated with exposure to environmental sources of methylmercury in the most susceptible human populations? How much methylmercury are humans exposed to, particularly women of child-bearing age and children among highly-exposed population groups? What is the magnitude of uncertainty and variability of mercury and methylmercury toxicokinetics in children?[152]
- What are the most effective means for informing susceptible populations of the health risks posed by mercury and methylmercury contamination of fish and seafood?[153]

EPA based the proposed and final §112(n) Revision Rule and the Clean Air Mercury Rule on the current state of the science.[154] In the context of these rules, EPA, among other things, identified the pertinent health endpoints associated with methylmercury contamination, considered the primary exposure pathways for ingestion of methylmercury, analyzed mercury control technologies, and considered the effectiveness and costs associated with reducing mercury emissions from coalfired power plants. EPA recognizes that there remain scientific uncertainties associated with some of the above-noted questions and is committed to continuing to work to advance the science in these areas.

Progress to date. Research results provide important information to support EPA's air, water, waste, and toxics programs in their ongoing efforts to address mercury. In recent years the major emphasis of research activities has been to support EPA's regulatory efforts to control mercury from coal-fired power plants, and to increase the Agency's understanding of mercury fate and transport. The following are major research results from the period 2001–2004.

EPA researchers have developed the methodology and instrumentation to make semi-continuous ambient measurements that distinguish among mercury forms—elemental gaseous mercury, divalent mercury (also referred to as reactive gaseous mercury [RGM]), and particulate phase mercury. The resulting speciated data have improved the understanding of atmospheric transport and fate and enhanced the ability to attribute the relative contributions of local, regional, and global sources of mercury to domestic and global deposition.[155]

EPA has produced a state-of-the-science atmospheric simulation model which incorporates the current understanding of chemical and physical processes involving mercury, including complex interactions with other atmospheric pollutants. This model uses highly efficient formulations and numerical methods, and has recently been used to simulate a full year of atmospheric mercury transport and fate over most of North America. Notwithstanding these recent advances in modeling atmospheric fate, transport, and deposition of mercury, there remain difficult scientific challenges to resolve. The Agency is currently working with international groups to better quantify atmospheric chemistry kinetics in Community Multiscale Air Quality (CMAQ) and to readily assess the impacts of these model adjustments to the fate, transport, and deposition of mercury.[156]

EPA has developed and tested mass balance models that use speciated atmospheric mercury deposition fluxes to calculate expected watershed mercury loadings, water body concentrations, and concentrations in fish. EPA's STAR grant research program, in addition to its research in other areas, has furthered the understanding of the reduction-oxidation balance between aquatic mercury and atmospheric mercury, and the effect of this cycling on the total mercury presence in freshwater and marine systems.

EPA's research program has provided extensive support to Agency program offices and the Administrator on mercury control technologies, including:

- Several comprehensive reports that document the development, cost and effectiveness of various mercury-specific control technology options (including sorbent injection), and evaluate co-control reductions that can be achieved using existing technologies including sulfur dioxide (SO2) scrubbers and selective catalytic reduction (SCR)-based nitrogen oxide (NOx) emissions control systems;[157]
- A White Paper, placed in EPA's coal-fired power plant rulemaking regulatory docket, summarizes the status of control technology options and outlines what can be achieved in the future using various alternative mercury removal technologies. This White Paper was updated to support EPA's Office of Air and Radiation and enable stakeholders to identify optimal management approaches.[158] In particular, these research results provide state agencies, industry, and others with the most current technology performance and cost information to inform their implementation decisions.

EPA has developed a report describing the impact of selected mercury control technologies on the characteristics of coal combustion residues and how selected utilization/disposal practices impact the fate of mercury residues. As part of this effort, ORD has generated a standard protocol that will be used to establish the leaching and thermal stability for the range of environmental conditions that coal combustion residues are exposed to during storage, land disposal, and use in commercial applications.[159]

EPA has evaluated the performance of continuous emission monitors (CEMs) for coal-fired power plant boilers as one possible tool for measuring total and speciated forms of mercury emitted from plants under different operating conditions.[160] Based on that evaluation, the Agency has concluded that CEMs are suitable regulatory tools. EPA's evaluation entailed a series of pilot-scale combustion experiments, representing realistic coal-fired power plant boiler measurement environments, that allowed controlled investigation of specific measurement issues associated with mercury CEM operation. Measurement results were obtained rapidly so that timely feedback could be provided to the monitor manufacturers in order to optimize their instruments. The improvements accomplished during the pilot-plant tests resulted in these same mercury CEMs participating in three full-scale utility boiler field evaluations that demonstrated their performance and capabilities. These results also apply to hazardous waste incinerators.

EPA has conducted a literature review to assess mercury methylation processes in aquatic sediments to inform selection and implementation of risk management strategies. This provided the technical foundation for subsequent products including a literature review of the sources and remediation of mercury-contaminated sediments and a model for evaluating the effects of remedial actions on mercury speciation and transport.[161] This work demonstrated how the introduction or exclusion of oxygen via risk management strategies impacted the fate and transport of mercury in sediments.

EPA has evaluated the effectiveness of several risk management strategies to address mercury-contaminated sediments, including dredging, capping, and monitored natural recovery. Work has focused on the Lavaca Bay, Texas Super-fund site.

EPA, as part of its effort to develop treatment alternatives for waste from sites contaminated with mercury mining wastes, has completed a study describing leaching profiles of mercury-containing waste rock and roaster tailings from a Superfund site in California.[162] These results were used to predict the fate and stability of mercury present, and will be used to assess the suitability of any applicable remediation treatment.

To support EPA's efforts to address issues associated with the long-term storage of mercury, the Agency has: (1) completed a report that describes a systematic method for comparing options for the long-term management of surplus elemental mercury in the U.S.,[163] and (2) collected information on state-of-the-art practices for macro-encapsulation and micro-encapsulation of mercury-contaminated hazardous wastes.

EPA has evaluated the effectiveness of some existing and future risk communication tools in a variety of formats, using 18 focus groups. Results show clear age, gender, and risk-related trends, which indicate that different risk communication tools will be required for each of these audiences, and that no one tool will be optimally effective across the board. The results of this work will be published in 2006/2007, and will add to the body of work outlining risk communication as an important tool for reducing environmental risk and protecting human health.

EPA is working with states to conduct research on fish tissue. For example, Region 8 has collected over 500 fish samples over the last three years from the Cheyenne River Sioux Tribal lands in stock ponds and in the Cheyenne, Moreau, and Missouri Rivers. Data from Region 8 showed that fish from small ponds have high levels of methylmercury. This may be a function of a biogeochemically favorable environment for methylmercury production (i.e., methylation of elemental mercury) in these environments, although further research is needed to confirm this hypothesis.

Region 8 has also used the data to determine Exposure Point Concentrations (EPC) for several species.[164] The regional office is working with the tribe to make recommendations on fish stocking in stock dams, and also on recommendations about how many meals per month should be eaten for each species according to the mercury EPC for that species.

Future focus and priority activities. EPA will continue to support the long-term goals described in the *Mercury Multi-Year Plan* and this *Roadmap*. The major emphasis of the mercury research program will continue to be the control of utility emissions, because utilities represent the most significant source of mercury release to the atmosphere in the United States.

- ***Toxic Metals Fate Report*** – EPA will develop a report on the fate of toxic metals from land disposal and commercial use of coal combustion residues from plants equipped with multipollutant control technologies. **Timeline: 2008**

HOW EPA WILL TRACK PROGRESS AND KEY TRENDS

1. **Air Emissions**
   - National Emissions Inventory (EPA)
     - EPA's primary source for air emissions data
   - Toxics Release Inventory (EPA)
2. **Ambient Air and Air Deposition**
   - Mercury Deposition Network (MDN) (joint federal/state program)
   - New England Mercury Monitoring Network (joint EPA/state program)
   - Long Range Transport Monitoring (joint EPA/NOAA activity)
3. **Water Quality/Fish Tissue**
   - National Fish Tissue Study (baseline study) (EPA)
   - National Listing of Fish Advisories (EPA)
   - National Coastal Assessment ecological monitoring (EPA)
   - Commercial fish monitoring (FDA)
4. **Human Biomonitoring**
   - National Health & Nutrition Examination Survey (CDC)

- *Sources of Mercury Emissions* – EPA will develop information on sources of mercury emissions including the regional/global atmospheric fate and transport of such emissions. **Timeline: 2008**
- *Integrated Multimedia Modeling* – EPA will develop an integrated multimedia modeling framework for the scientific understanding of mercury. **Timeline: 2010**

Mercury Monitoring Overview

There are many ongoing monitoring projects and programs that measure mercury in various media. These projects and programs are conducted by other federal agencies, states and tribal governments, and in academia. Access to routine, ongoing monitoring information is needed to track environmental and health trends and to measure program effectiveness.

A basic strategy for routine mercury monitoring is to focus on the most efficient points to monitor along the major transport and exposure path of air-to-water-to-fish-to-humans, in order to determine trends in environmental and health levels and whether they are responding to control and reduction measures. Based on this mercury transport and exposure path, the four most important media of concern are: (1) air emissions, (2) ambient air and air deposition, (3) fish tissue, and (4) human tissue. The Centers for Disease Control and Prevention (CDC) collects data on human tissue, which includes blood, hair, and urine. Data on emissions and deposition allow EPA to detect changes quickly that reflect program activities with great relevance to long-term health and the environment. Data on fish and human tissue allow EPA to measure longer-term changes that are slower to respond to control measures but are better indicators of environmental quality and human health. EPA will continue to work with other federal agencies, states, and tribal governments to coordinate and enhance data collection for these four key indicators of long-term trends and program results for mercury.

Progress to date. Much progress has been made by EPA and others to establish monitoring and reporting systems to collect data on mercury releases and contamination. During the last five years, in particular, EPA has encouraged and supported increased national monitoring of mercury in both fish tissue and human blood and hair samples, which is discussed in more detail below. The following discussion provides information on current monitoring programs conducted or supported by EPA, and on recent EPA reports that highlight significant new data from various mercury monitoring activities.

Air Emissions Monitoring

Atmospheric transport is the primary focus for mercury monitoring and modeling, as it is the dominant means for cycling mercury from anthropogenic sources, such as coal-fired power plant combustion sources, into other media. Emissions inventories provide information about the sources of mercury, and the relative contributions of those sources to total releases. Routine air emissions monitoring is needed to track long-term trends of mercury emissions over time and geographic space in the U.S. Such information is essential to evaluating the success of EPA's programs for reducing mercury air emissions from specific sources.

Two key EPA reporting efforts for air emissions are the *National Emissions Inventory (NEI)* and the *Toxics Release Inventory (TRI)*. These databases have been modified and improved over time so that the Agency has the latest information necessary to measure program effectiveness and track environmental trends. (For further information, see Section I.)

Ambient Air and Air Deposition Monitoring

Both ambient air monitoring and air deposition networks provide information on mercury once it has been emitted. This monitoring information is needed to track long-term mercury contamination in ambient air, and to provide input to ongoing research and modeling activities to improve scientific understanding of mercury transport and fate in the environment; stationary and mobile sources of mercury; and the relative contributions of those sources to total mercury releases to the environment.

Major routine monitoring activities for mercury in ambient air and air deposition include the following:

- *Mercury Deposition Network (MDN)*[165] – Formed in 1995, the MDN is part of the National Atmospheric Deposition Program/National Trends Network (NADP/NTN), a nationwide network of over 70 precipitation monitoring sites that collect weekly data on the chemistry of precipitation for monitoring of long-term geographical and temporal trends. The network is a cooperative effort among state agricultural experiment stations, the U.S. Geological Survey, U.S. Department of Agriculture, EPA, and numerous other governmental and private entities. Information from the MDN is being used to develop a national database of weekly concentrations of total mercury in precipitation and the seasonal and annual flux of total mercury in wet deposition. However, there are some gaps in the current geographic coverage of MDN which may limit the analysis. Also, the MDN does not collect data on dry deposition for either elemental or divalent mercury. At present, no adequate field routine measurement method exists. EPA and others recognize that dry deposition data are important—in some areas such data are as important as wet deposition in understanding total deposition. For these reasons, EPA announced in December 2005 a request for proposals to stimulate development of such methods.

- *New England Mercury Monitoring Network* – EPA and the New England states have established a mercury monitoring network. A number of monitoring field studies have been initiated in New England to measure mercury deposition and ambient concentration of atmospheric mercury. These studies provide baseline information on mercury deposition to support regional efforts to control mercury contamination and to evaluate the ecological effects of mercury contamination.

- ***Long Range Transport Monitoring*** – EPA, in collaboration with the U.S. National Oceanic and Atmospheric Administration (NOAA), is working with other countries on characterization, modeling, and speciation of ambient and source level mercury related to mercury emissions transport and deposition on local, regional, and global scales. As part of this effort, high and low altitude monitoring is being conducted at various sites, including Mauna Loa, Hawaii. (For further information, see Section V.)

Fish Tissue Monitoring

Monitoring of fish tissue provides essential information about the levels of mercury consumed by the human population. Routine monitoring of marine and freshwater fish consumed in the U.S. diet is needed to track trends in the level of likely mercury exposure by the U.S. population, as well as trends in mercury concentrations in fish in U.S. water bodies over time and geographic space. Information on mercury concentrations in fish tissue from U.S. water bodies is essential to evaluating the success of EPA's programs for addressing mercury releases from air, water, and land sources. EPA has recently developed a new water quality criterion for mercury that is based on the amount of mercury found in fish tissue rather than the amount in water bodies. Fish tissue data are also needed as input to research and modeling activities to improve scientific understanding of mercury transport and fate in the environment; sources of mercury in water bodies; and the relative contributions of those sources to total mercury releases to the environment.

Many governmental organizations provide important monitoring data on fish, such as FDA's commercial fish monitoring program.[166] EPA's major monitoring activities include the following:

- ***EPA's National Lake Fish Tissue Study***[167] – The National Study of Chemical Residues in Lake Fish Tissue (or National Lake Fish Tissue Study) is being conducted by EPA's Office of Water (OW). It is a one-time screening-level study to sample contaminants in fish tissue in freshwater lakes and reservoirs in the contiguous U.S., including mercury as well as other chemicals. EPA will use the study results to develop the first national estimates of the mean concentrations of mercury and 267 other chemicals in lake fish, to define a national fish contamination baseline to track progress of pollution control activities, and to identify areas where contaminant levels are high enough to warrant further investigation. Sampling has been conducted for four years at a total of 500 locations, or about 125 sites annually. EPA has worked with 47 states, three tribes and two other federal agencies to collect fish for the study. While planning for the study began in 1998, fish sampling began in 2000 and ended in November 2003. EPA has released all 4 years of raw data to the public. Agency analysis of the cumulative 4-year data set will be completed, and the final report will be completed in December 2006.

- *EPA's National Listing of Fish Advisories*[168] – This database contains all fish advisory information provided to EPA by the states, tribes, and Canada. It also contains information on mercury in fish tissue that states and tribes collect as part of their fish advisory programs. States monitor their waters by sampling fish tissue for persistent pollutants that bioaccumulate. States issue their guidelines voluntarily and have flexibility in what criteria they use and how the data are collected. As a result, there are significant variations in the number of waters tested, the pollutants tested for and the threshold for issuing advisories. Based on self-reporting, the national trend is for states to monitor different waters each year, generally without retesting waters monitored in previous years. States issue fish consumption advisories to the public if elevated concentrations of chemicals such as mercury are found in local fish. EPA makes information about fish advisories easily accessible to the public on its website.

- *EPA's Ecological Monitoring to Characterize the Condition of U.S. Estuarine Resources* – As part of its National Coastal Assessment, EPA's Office of Research and Development seeks to characterize the ecological condition of U.S. estuarine resources through the collection and analysis of fish tissue for mercury (and various other contaminants) from estuaries throughout the U.S., at about 35–100 sites per year for each of twenty-three coastal states and Puerto Rico. The National Coastal Assessment data is a relatively new program in the Office of Research and Development, which is beginning to provide information on fish tissue toxics concentrations from selected U.S. estuaries. ORD is currently reviewing these data to determine their usefulness for integration with existing EPA approaches for assessing fish tissue mercury concentrations and their changes over time due to both emissions and deposition changes.

States are also actively engaged in monitoring fish levels of methylmercury in their waters. For example, the Alaska Department of Environmental Conservation has been conducting a multi-year study of safety of fish and seafood resources in Alaska waters with respect to contaminants. EPA Region 10 secured funding for Alaska to perform additional PBT organic analyses, including methylmercury, and a final report is pending. This monitoring project is ongoing.

Human Biomonitoring

Routine monitoring of human tissue samples is needed to track long-term trends in the levels of mercury exposure of people in the U.S. over time and geographic space. CDC collects data on human tissue, including blood, hair, and urine. Such human biomonitoring may be the most meaningful long-term indicator of the effectiveness of programs for reducing risks associated with mercury releases and exposure. It is also useful in setting priorities for future research and for risk communication strategies and activities to reduce mercury exposure in the short-term.

The level of methylmercury in blood is the best available indicator of human exposure to methylmercury through fish consumption. Mercury blood levels in women of childbearing age is an especially useful indicator of mercury exposure, since this measure indicates both the actual exposure of adult women and the potential for exposure of fetuses through the transfer of maternal blood through the placenta. Other types of human tissue have been sampled for mercury such as hair, but so far they have been found less useful than blood levels. At the present time there is insufficient understanding of the relationship of mercury in blood and hair to mercury levels found in these other tissues.[169]

The only source of nationwide information on methylmercury in humans is the *National Health and Nutrition Examination Survey (NHANES)*, which is conducted by the U.S. Centers for Disease Control and Prevention (CDC) with financial support from EPA and other agencies. NHANES is a continuous survey of the health and nutritional status of the civilian, non-institutionalized U.S. population, and data are released and reported in 2-year cycles.[170]

In 1999 NHANES began measuring mercury levels in blood, hair, and urine for the first time in a national sample of childbearing-aged women and in children aged 1–5 years in the U.S. The CDC's report, published in 2003, provided the first nationally representative estimates of U.S. women's and children's exposures to mercury based on biologic measures.[171]

In November 2004, the CDC published an updated summary of NHANES data for the four-year period 1999 to 2002.[172] These updated findings confirm that blood mercury levels in women of childbearing age are usually below levels of concern, but that approximately six percent of childbearing-aged women had levels at or above EPA's Reference Dose (RfD).

CDC plans to continue this NHANES mercury monitoring in future years. NHANES 2005–2006 will include measurements of mercury species (methyl, ethyl, and inorganic) in blood in order to define more precisely the exposure to various sources of mercury. Blood mercury levels will be measured in persons (male and female) one-year and older, while urinary mercury will be measured in persons six years of age and older.[173]

Recent EPA Reports Utilizing Mercury Monitoring Data

- *America's Children and the Environment: Measures of Contaminants, Body Burden, and Illness[174]* – Published in February 2003, this is EPA's second report on trends in environmental factors related to the health and well-being of children in the U.S. The report brings together, in one place, quantitative information from a variety of sources to show trends in levels of environmental contaminants in air, water, food, and soil; concentrations of contaminants measured in the bodies of children and women; and childhood illnesses that may be influenced by exposure to environmental contaminants. This second report provides mercury information for the first time. The section on body burdens includes a new measure of mercury in the blood of women of child-bearing age, using NHANES data. A new section on emerging issues presents information about important aspects of children's environmental health for which data had recently become available, including mercury in fish as an important source of mercury exposure for people in the U.S.

- *EPA's Draft Report on the Environment 2003[175]* – Published in June 2003, the report presents EPA's first national picture of the U.S. environment, including mercury contamination. This report was the first step in the Agency's Environmental Indicators Initiative, launched in November 2001, which seeks to identify better indicators that EPA can use to measure and track the state of the environment and support improved environmental decisionmaking.

Future focus and priority activities. EPA will continue to need reliable sources of routine mercury monitoring data. Since monitoring activities are resource intensive, EPA will continue its current strategy of focusing primarily on monitoring for a small number of key environmental and health indicators, and to leverage resources by looking for opportunities to collaborate with other governmental and non-governmental entities where appropriate. In addition, the Agency plans to publish the following documents:

- *Final Results of EPA's National Lake Fish Tissue Study* – The final report will be published in 2006. EPA will use the study results to develop the first national estimate of mean concentrations for mercury and 267 other chemicals in fish, to provide a baseline to track progress of pollution control activities, and to identify areas where contaminant levels are high enough to warrant further investigation.
- *EPA's Report on the Environment 2007* – Under EPA's Environmental Indicators Initiative, the Agency will continue working to identify better indicators that EPA can use to measure and track the state of the environment and support improved environmental decisionmaking. The next report to present a national picture of the U.S. environment, planned for publication in 2007, will be providing additional emphasis on mercury indicators and information.

End Notes

[1] EPA, 1999a. 1999 National Emissions Inventory Documentation and Data—Final Version 3.0. Accessible at: www.epa.gov/ttn/chief/net/1999inventory.html.

[2] EPA, 2005c. U.S. Environmental Protection Agency. National Listing of Fish Advisories. Fact Sheet, Sep. 2005. EPA-823-F-05-004. Accessible at: http://epa.gov/waterscience/fish/advisories/fs2004.pdf.

[3] RIA, Regulatory Impact Analysis, Clean Air Mercury Rule. EPA, 2005. Accessible at: http://epa.gov/ttn/atw/utility/TSC-112final.pdf.

[4] NRC, 2000. National Research Council. Toxicological Effects of Methylmercury. Committee on The Toxicological Effects of Methyl-mercury, Board on Environmental Studies and Toxicology. Accessible at: http://books.nap.edu/books/0309071402/html/1.html.

[5] EPA and FDA, 2004. What You Need to Know About Mercury in Fish and Shellfish. EPA-823-F-04-009. Accessible at: www.epa.gov/waterscience/fishadvice/advice.html.

[6] EPA, 2005a. Technical Support Document, Revision of December 2000 Regulatory Finding on the Emissions of Hazardous Air Pollutants From Electric Utility Steam Generating Units and the Removal of Coaland Oil-Fired Electric Utility Steam Generating Units from the §112(c) List: Reconsideration, Oct. 21, 2005. Accessible at: www.epa.gov/ttn/atw/utility/TSC-112finaL.pdf.

[7] A Community Multiscale Air Quality (CMAQ) modeling run was performed to estimate the impact of global sources on U.S. deposition estimates. For this analysis, all non-U.S.

mercury input species to the model were set to zero. By comparing the results of this analysis with the 2001 Clean Air Mercury Rule (CAMR) base case run, which included all U.S. and global mercury species, the percent of total mercury deposition attributable to global sources can be estimated. The model estimated that over 80 percent of total mercury deposition in the U.S. is attributable to global sources.

Due to the evolving nature of mercury modeling science, such deposition estimates have associated uncertainties. For example, it remains difficult to distinguish between the natural emissions of mercury and the re-emission of previously deposited anthropogenic mercury and there remains uncertainty in the scientific community concerning the atmospheric processes that control the oxidation state of atmospheric mercury. Thus, further advances in the current understanding of mercury chemistry could potentially lead to changes in the modeling parameters and assumptions governing the mercury chemistry in the models and therefore, changes in the estimate of the fraction deposited in the U.S. attributable to global sources.

[8] EPA, 1999a. U.S. Environmental Protection Agency. 1999 National Emissions Inventory Documentation and Data—Final Version 3.0. Accessible at: www.epa.gov/ttn/chief/net/1999inventory.html.

[9] Jasinski, S.M. 1994. The Materials Flow of Mercury in the United States. U.S. Bureau of Mines, Information Circular 9412. Accessible at: http://pubs.usgs.gov/usbmic/ic-9412/.

[10] EPA, 1999a, and UNEP 2002. United Nations Environment Programme. Global Mercury Assessment. Accessible at: www.chem.unep.ch/mercury/report/GMA-report-TOC.htm.

[11] CDC, 2005. Centers for Disease Control. Mercury, pp. 45-51 in Third National Report on Human Exposure to Environmental Chemicals. Accessible at: www.cdc.gov/exposurereport/3rd/downloads.htm.

[12] NRC, 2000. National Research Council. Toxicological Effects of Methylmercury. Committee on The Toxicological Effects of Methyl-mercury, Board on Environmental Studies and Toxicology. Accessible at: http://books.nap.edu/books/0309071402/html/1.html.

EPA, 2001a. Reference Dose for Chronic Oral Exposure (RfD)—Methylmercury, last revised 7/21/01. Integrated Risk Information System (IRIS). Accessible at: www.epa.gov/iris/subst/0073.htm#reforal.

[13] FDA. U.S. Food and Drug Administration. Mercury in Fish: FDA Monitoring Program. For information, see: www.cfsan.fda.gov/~frf/seamehg2.html.

[14] EPA, 2005a. Technical Support Document, Revision of December 2000 Regulatory Finding on the Emissions of Hazardous Air Pollutants From Electric Utility Steam Generating Units and the Removal of Coaland Oil-Fired Electric Utility Steam Generating Units from the §112(c) List: Reconsideration, Oct. 21, 2005. Accessible at: www.epa.gov/ttn/atw/utility/TSC-112final.pdf.

[15] EPA, 1997. Mercury Study Report to Congress. EPA-452/R-97-003, December 1997. Accessible at: www.epa.gov/ttn/oarpg/t3/reports/volume1/pdf.

[16] EPA, 1998. Study of hazardous air pollutant emissions from electric utility steam generating units—Final Report to Congress. EPA-453/R-98-004a&b, February 1998.

[17] EPA. Area Source Standards. For information, see: www.epa.gov/ttn/atw/urban/arearules.html.

[18] EPA. Residual Risk Program. For information, see: www.epa.gov/ttn/atw/rrisk/residriskpg.html.

[19] EPA, 1997.

[20] LWA, 2002. Larry Walker Associates. Mercury Source Control and Pollution Prevention Evaluation, Final Report, March 2002, amended July 2002. Prepared for: Association of Metropolitan Sewerage Agencies. Accessible at: www.amsa-cleanwater.org/advocacy/mercgrant/finalreport.pdf.

[21] EPA, 2005b. 2003 Toxics Release Inventory (TRI) Public Data Release eReport, May 2005. Accessible at: www.epa.gov/tri/tridata/tri03/2003eReport.pdf.

[22] EPA, 2005b.

[23] EPA, 2005b.

[24] Jasinski, S.M., 1994. The Materials Flow of Mercury in the United States. U.S. Bureau of Mines, Information Circular 9412. Accessible at: http://pubs.usgs.gov/usbmic/ic-9412/.

[25] Lawrence, Bruce, 2001. Bethlehem Apparatus Company, Inc. Personal communication, June 22, 2001.

[26] H2E. Hospitals for a Healthy Environment. For information, see: www.h2e-online.org/.

[27] Maxson, P.A., 2004. Mercury Flows Report: Mercury Flows in Europe and the World, The Impact of Decommissioned Chloralkali Plants. European Commission. Accessible at: http://europa.eu.int/comm/environment/chemicals/mercury/pdf/report.pdf.

[28] Quicksilver Caucus, 2003. Mercury Stewardship Storage of Mercury, Review Draft, February, 2003. Accessible at: www.sso.org/ecos/Quick%20silver%20documents/RD%20QSC-STOR %20Mar-03.pdf.

[29] EPA, 2005f. Economic and Environmental Analysis of Technologies to Treat Mercury and Dispose in a Waste Containment Facility. See: www.epa.gov/ORD/NRMRL/pubs/ 600r05157/600r05157.pdf.

[30] EPA and FDA, 2004. What You Need to Know About Mercury in Fish and Shellfish. EPA-823-F-04-009. Accessible at: www.epa.gov/waterscience/fishadvice/advice.html.

[31] EPA. Mercury Web site. For information, see: www.epa.gov/mercury/.

[32] EPA, 2005a.

[33] UNEP, 2002. United Nations Environment Programme. Global Mercury Assessment. Accessible at: www.chem.unep.ch/mercury/Report/GMA-report-TOC.htm.

[34] UNEP, 2005. Results of the Governing Council's discussions on chemicals management, including mercury programme, at its 23rd session in February, 2005. Accessible at: www.chem.unep.ch/mercury/GC23-results.htm.

[35] EPA, 2000. Mercury Research Strategy. EPA-600-R-00-073. Accessible at: http://cfpub.epa. gov/ncea/cfm/recordisplay.cfm?deid=20853.

[36] "EPA Releases 12th Annual National Listing of Fish Advisories." Press release. August 24, 2004.

[37] EPA, 2005c. U.S. Environmental Protection Agency. National Listing of Fish Advisories. Fact Sheet, Sep. 2005. EPA-823-F-05-004. Accessible at: http://epa.gov/waterscience/fish/ advisories/fs2004.pdf.

[38] Table 1: National Air Emissions Inventory for Mercury. Source: EPA, 1999a.

[39] Figure 1: The Mercury Cycle. Adapted from EPA, 1997. Mercury Study Report to Congress. EPA-452/R-97-003, December 1997. Accessible at: www.epa.gov/ttn/oarpg/t3/reports/ volume1.pdf.

[40] EPA, 2001a.
NRC, 2000. National Research Council. Toxicological Effects of Methylmercury. Committee on The Toxicological Effects of Methylmercury, Board on Environmental Studies and Toxicology. Accessible at: http://books.nap.edu/books/0309071402/html/1.html.

[41] EPA, 1997. Mercury Study Reprot to Congress. EPA-452/R-97-003, December 1997. Accessible at: www.epa.gov/ttn/oarpg/t3/reports/volume1.pdf.

[42] EPA, 1997.

[43] EPA, 1997.

[44] EPA, 2005a. Technical Support Document, Revision of December 2000 Regulatory Finding on the Emissions of Hazardous Air Pollutants From Electric Utility Steam Generating Units and the Removal of Coaland Oil-Fired Electric Utility Steam Generating Units from the §112(c) List: Reconsideration, Oct. 21, 2005. Accessible at: www.epa.gov/ttn/atw/ utility/TSC-112finaL.pdf.

[45] A Community Multiscale Air Quality (CMAQ) modeling run was performed to estimate the impact of global sources on U.S. deposition estimates. For this analysis, all non-U.S. mercury input species to the model were set to zero. By comparing the results of this analysis with the 2001 Clean Air Mercury Rule (CAMR) base case run, which included all U.S. and global mercury species, the percent of total mercury deposition attributable to

global sources can be estimated. The model estimated that over 80 percent of total mercury deposition in the U.S. is attributable to global sources.

Due to the evolving nature of mercury modeling science, such deposition estimates have associated uncertainties. For example, it remains difficult to distinguish between the natural emissions of mercury and the re-emission of previously deposited anthropogenic mercury and there remains uncertainty in the scientific community concerning the atmospheric processes that control the oxidation state of atmospheric mercury. Thus, further advances in the current understanding of mercury chemistry could potentially lead to changes in the modeling parameters and assumptions governing the mercury chemistry in the models and therefore, changes in the estimate of the fraction deposited in the U.S. attributable to global sources.

[46] EPA, 2005a.

[47] EPA, 1999a. 1999 National Emissions Inventory Documentation and Data—Final Version 3.0. Accessible at: www.epa.gov/ttn/chief/net/1999inventory.html.

[48] EPA, 1999a.

[49] Table 1: National Air Emissions Inventory for Mercury. Source: EPA, 1999a.

[50] President's Clear Skies Legislation of 2003. For information, see: www.epa.gov/air/clearskies/.

[51] EPA. Clean Air Act rules on mercury emissions. For information on EPA's activities to control power plant emissions, see: www.epa.gov/mercury/control_emissions/index.htm.

[52] EPA, 1999b. Residual Risk Report to Congress. EPA 453/R-99-001, March 1999. Accessible at: www.epa.gov/ttn/oarpg/t3/reports/risk_rep.pdf.

For information about EPA's Residual Risk Program, see: www.epa.gov/ttn/atw/ rrisk/ residriskpg.html.

[53] EPA. Nevada Mining Partnership Program. For information, see: www.epa.gov/Region9/ cross_pr/innovations/mining.html.

[54] EPA, 2004a. 2003 Report on Success of Voluntary Mercury Reduction Program (VMRP) with Nevada Gold Mines, October, 2004. Accessible at: www.epa.gov/region9/toxic/mercury/ goldmine.pdf.

[55] 64 Federal Register 38705, 7/19/99.

[56] EPA. Area Source Standards. For information, see: ww.epa.gov/ttn/atw/urban/arearules.html.

[57] Ecology Center, 2001. Ecology Center, Great Lakes United, and University of Tennessee Center for Clean Products and Clean Technologies. Toxics in Vehicles: Mercury. Accessible at: www.cleancarcampaign.org/pdfs/toxicsinvehicles_mercury.pdf.

[58] The estimate is based on data gathered from industry by EPA during the initial phase of EAF area source rulemaking which is still under development.

[59] EPA. National Pollutant Discharge Elimination System (NPDES) Permits. For information about this program, see: http://cfpub.epa.gov/npdes/.

[60] Alpers, C.N. and M.P. Hunerlach, 2000. Mercury contamination from historic gold mining in California. USGS Fact Sheet FS- 061-00. Accessible at: http://ca.water.usgs.gov/mercury/ fs06100.html.

[61] EPA, 2005b. 2003 Toxics Release Inventory (TRI) Public Data Release eReport, May, 2005. Accessible at: www.epa.gov/tri/tridata/tri03/2003eReport.pdf.

[62] EPA, 2005b.

[63] EPA, 2001b. Water Quality Criterion for the Protection of Human Health: Methylmercury. EPA-823-R01-001. Accessible at: www.epa.gov/waterscience/criteria/methylmercury/.

[64] EPA, 2001a.

[65] 40 Code of Federal Regulations 130.7.

[66] These statistics were compiled from data received by EPA and available on its Total Maximum Daily Loads (TMDL) webpage accessible at: http://oaspub.epa.gov/waters/national_ rept.control.

[67] EPA, 2005c.

[68] EPA, 2001b.

[69] These statistics were compiled from data received by EPA and available on its TMDL webpage accessible at: http://oaspub.epa.gov/waters/national_rept.control.

[70] 40 Code of Federal Regulations 132 Table 4.

[71] The average was developed by EPA based on effluent data reported by the EPA Region 5 states: Illinois, Indiana, Ohio, Michigan, Minnesota and Wisconsin. States discuss effluent data in reports on their web sites. For example: Michigan: www.michigan.gov/deq/0,1607, 7-135-3313_3686_3728-11384—,00.html.Wisconsin: http://dnr.wi.gov/org/caer/cea/ mercury/potw.htm. Minnesota: www.pca.state.mn.us/water/tmdl/tmdl-mercuryplan.html.

[72] Cocca, P. 2001. Mercury Maps: National Report on Human Exposure to Environmental Chemicals. Publication No. 01-0379.

[73] Clean Water Act (Federal Water Pollution Control Act, as amended) §307(b); 33 United States Code §1317.

[74] LWA, 2002. Larry Walker Associates. Mercury Source Control and Pollution Prevention Evaluation, Final Report, March 2002, amended July 2002. Prepared for: Association of Metropolitan Sewerage Agencies. Accessible at: www.amsa-cleanwater.org/advocacy/ mercgrant/finalreport.pdf.

[75] San Francisco Public Utilities Commission. For information about the San Francisco Dental Mercury Reduction Program, see: http://sfwater.org/main.cfm/MC_ID/4/MSC_ID/85.

[76] EPA, 2005b.

[77] Surface impoundments include natural topographic depressions, man-made excavations and diked areas that primarily are made of earthen materials and which hold liquid wastes. These uncovered areas are commonly used to volatilize and/or settle materials. Other surface impoundments are surface impoundments other than those which are authorized under the Resource Conservation and Recovery Act (RCRA) to accept hazardous waste for disposal.

[78] Other land disposal is the disposal of the toxic chemical to land at the facility that does not fall into one of the other on-site land release categories found in Section 5.5.1 through 5.5.3 of the TRI Form R. Other disposal includes such activities as placement in waste piles and spills or leaks. Data from Section 5.5.4 on the TRI Form R.

[79] Mercury -Containing and Rechargeable Battery Act, 42 United States Code 14301, and EPA Universal Waste Rule. For information, see: www.epa.gov/epaoswer/hazwaste/id/univwast/ regs.htm.

[80] EPA. Municipal Incinerator Rules. For information about Large Municipal Waste Combustors, see:www.epa.gov/ttn/atw/129/mwc/rimwc.html. For information about Small Municipal Waste Combustors, see: www.epa.gov/ttn/atw/129/mwc/rimwc2.html.

[81] EPA. Universal Waste Regulations. For information, see: www.epa.gov/epaoswer/hazwaste/ id/univwast/regs.htm.

[82] 70 Federal Register 45508, 8/5/05.

[83] EPA. Superfund National Priorities List. For information on NPL Site Listing Process, see: www.epa.gov/superfund/sites/npl/npl_hrs.htm.

[84] EPA. RCRA Corrective Action Program. For information on the program, see: www.epa.gov/epaoswer/hazwaste/ca/backgnd.htm#5.

[85] Maine. An Act to Prevent Mercury Emissions When Recycling and Disposing of Motor Vehicles. Provision to remove mercury switches found at Sec. 3.38 Me.Rev.Stat.Ann.tit. §1665-A.3. Accessible at: http://janus.state.me.us/legis/ros/lom/LOM120th/5Pub651-700/Pub651-700-05.htm.

[86] Ecology Center, 2001.

[87] EPA, 2005d. Clean Air Mercury Rule (CAMR) and Clean Air Interstate Rule (CAIR). For information, see: www.epa.gov/air/mercuryrule/.

[88] 69 Federal Register 21198, 4/20/04.

[89] 68 Federal Register 70903, 12/19/03.

[90] 69 Federal Register 21906, 4/22/04.

[91] Cocca, P. 2001.64 Federal Register 38705, 7/19/99.

[92] Jasinski, S.M., 1994. The Materials Flow of Mercury in the United States. U.S. Bureau of Mines, Information Circular 9412. Accessible at: http://pubs.usgs.gov/usbmic/ic-9412/.

[93] Figure 3: Total 2001 U.S. Mercury Use in Products. Source: Lawrence, Bruce, 2001. Bethlehem Apparatus Company, Inc. Personal communication, June 22, 2001.

[94] Lawrence, 2001 and The Chlorine Institute, Inc., 2-006.

[95] Figure 4: U.S. Mercury Product and Process Use Trends. Sources: For 1980 through 1997: USGS. U.S. Geological Survey. Minerals Yearbook: Mercury, 1994–2001. Accessible at: http://minerals.usgs.gov/minerals/pubs/commodity/mercury/. For 2001: Lawrence, 2001 and The Chlorine Institute, Inc., 2006.

[96] Environment Canada and EPA, 1997. The Great Lakes Binational Toxics Strategy. Accessible at:www.epa.gov/glnpo/p2/bns.html.

[97] Environment Canada and EPA, 2004. Great Lakes Binational Toxics Strategy 2004 Annual Progress Report. Accessible at:http://binational.net/bns/2004/index.html.

[98] The Chlorine Institute, Inc., 2006. Ninth Annual Report to EPA for the Year 2005, May 15, 2006. Accessible at:www.epa.gov/region5/air/mercury/9thcl2report.pdf.

[99] H2E. Hospitals for a Healthy Environment. For information, see: www.h2e-online.org/.

[100] For information about legislation to reduce mercury in the New England states, see: IMERC. Interstate Mercury Education and Reduction Clearinghouse at: www.newmoa.org/newmoa/ntdocs/prevention/mercury/imerc.cfm.

[101] Conference of New England Governors and Eastern Canadian Premiers, 2002. Summary of School Mercury Programs in New England and Eastern Canada. August 2002. Accessible at: www.cap-cpma.ca/images/pdf/eng/10-mtf_school_survey_e.pdf.

[102] The Chlorine Institute, Inc., 2006.

[103] IMERC. For information, see: www.newmoa.org/Newmoa/htdocs/prevention/mercury/imerc.cfm.

[104] EPA. Environmentally Preferable Purchasing, Database of Environmental Information for Products and Services. For information, see: http://yosemite1.epa.gov/oppt/eppstand2.nsf/Pages/Homepage.html?Open.

[105] EPA. Green Suppliers Network. For information, see: www.epa.gov/p2/programs/gsn.htm.

[106] EPA. Schools Chemical Cleanout Campaign (SC3). For information, see: www.epa.gov/epaoswer/osw/conserve/clusters/schools/index.htm.

[107] EPA. National Partnership for Environmental Priorities (NPEP) Program, The Mercury Challenge. For information, see: www.epa.gov/epaoswer/hazwaste/minimize/mercchall.htm.

[108] Lawrence, Bruce, 2002. Bethlehem Apparatus Company, Inc. World Mercury Market(s) From the Supply Side. Presentation at conference: Breaking the Mercury Cycle, Boston, MA, May 1–3, 2002. Accessible at: www.newmoa.org/Newmoa/htdocs/prevention/mercury/breakingcycle/toc.cfm.

[109] Maxson, P.A., 2004 Mercury Flows Report: Mercury Flows in Europe and the World, The Impact of Decommissioned Chloralkali Plants. European Commission. Accessible at: http://europa.eu.int/comm/environment/chemicals/mercury/pdf/report.pdf.

[110] Maxson, 2004.

[111] The Chlorine Institute, Inc., 2006.

[112] 69 Federal Register 23733, 4/30/04.

[113] Quicksilver Caucus, 2003. Mercury Stewardship Storage of Mercury, October 2003. Accessible at: www.ecos.org/files/721_file_QSC_STOR_Oct_03.pdf

[114] EPA, 2005f. Economic and Environmental Analysis of Technologies to Treat Mercury and Dispose in a Waste Containment Facility. See: www.epa.gov/ORD/NRMRL/pubs/600r05157/600r05157.pdf.

[115] EPA. Mercury Laws and Regulations. For information on how mercury is regulated under RCRA, see: www.epa.gov/epaoswer/hazwaste/mercury/reg_stand.htm.

[116] Figure 1: The Mercury Cycle. Adapted from EPA, 1997. Mercury Study Report to Congress. EPA-452/R-97-003, December 1997. Accessible at: www.epa.gov/ttn/oarpg/t3/reports/volume1.pdf.

[117] EPA and FDA, 2004. What You Need to Know About Mercury in Fish and Shellfish. EPA-823-F-04-009. Accessible at: www.epa.gov/waterscience/fishadvice/advice.html.

[118] EPA, 2005c.

[119] "EPA Releases 12th Annual National Listing of Fish Advisories." Press release. August 24, 2004.

[120] EPA, 2002a. Task Force on Ritualistic Uses of Mercury Report, Dec. 2002. EPA-540-R-01-005. Accessible at: www.epa.gov/superfund/action/community/mercury.pdf.

[121] EPA. Mercury Web site. For information, see: www.epa.gov/mercury/.

[122] Minnesota Pollution Control Agency. Mercury-Free Zone Program. For information, see: www.pca.state.mn.us/programs/mercury-free/.

[123] Figure 5: Where are Man-Made Mercury Emissions Originating? Source of figure: Pacyna, J., S. Wilson, F. Steenhuisen and E. Pacyna. 2005. Spatially Distributed Inventories of Global Anthropogenic Emissions of Mercury to the Atmosphere. Accessible at: (www.amap.no/Resources/HgEmissions/). Original figure presented courtesy of AMAP, Arctic Monitoring and Assessment Programme, Oslo, Norway.

[124] EPA, 2005a.

[125] Figure 6: Man-Made Air Emissions of Mercury: Distribution by Region in 1990 and 2000. Source: Pacyna, J. and J. Munthe, 2004. Summary of research projects on mercury conducted by researchers in Norway and Sweden. Presentation at Workshop on Mercury, Brussels, March 29–30, 2004. Accessible at: www.ivl.se/nytt/konferenser/mercury/pacyna.pdf.

[126] UNEP, 2002. United Nations Environment Programme. Global Mercury Assessment. Accessible at: www.chem.unep.ch/mercury/Report/GMA-report-TOC.htm.

[127] EPA estimate based on UNEP 2002.

[128] EIA, 2004. Energy Information Administration. International Energy Outlook 2004 (annual report). Report #DOE/EIA- 0484(2004), April, 2004. Accessible at: www.eia.doe.gov/oiaf/ieo/.

[129] UNEP, 2002.

[130] Veiga, M. and R. Baker, 2004. Protocols for Environmental and Health Assessment of Mercury Released by Artisanal and Smallscale Gold Miners, Report to the Global Mercury Project: Removal to Barriers of Introduction to Cleaner Artisanal Gold Mining and Extraction Technologies, GEF/UNDP/UNIDO, Vienna, Austria, 170. Accessible at: www.unites.uqam.ca/gmf/intranet/gmp/files/doc/gmp/Protocols_for_Environmental%20_Assessment_2005_08_11.pdf.

[131] Veiga, M.M. and J.J. Hinton, 2002. Abandoned Artisanal Gold Mines in the Brazilian Amazon: A Legacy of Mercury Pollution. Natural Resources Forum, February, 2002.

[132] UNEP, 2002.

[133] This estimate is based on communication with The Chlorine Institute and review of the following two pamphlets: The Chlorine Institute, Inc., 2004b. Pamphlet 10, North American Chlor-Alkali Industry Plants and Production Data Report 2003, Updated June, 2004. The Chlorine Institute, Inc., 2004c. Pamphlet 16, Chlor-Alkali Plants Outside North America, Updated October 2004.

[134] Source of 2,000 estimate is Lawrence, 2002. Source of 3,400 estimate is Maxson, 2004.

[135] Figure 7: Global Mercury Consumption, 2000. Source: Maxson, 2004.

[136] Environment Canada and EPA, 2005. Great Lakes Binational Toxics Strategy: Assessment of Level 1 Substances, Summary Report. Accessible at: http://binational.net/bns/2005/iindex.html.

[137] Conference of New England Governors/Eastern Canadian Premiers, 2003. Report to the New England Governors and Eastern Canadian Premiers on Mercury Projects, August 2003. Accessible at: http://cap-cpma.ca/images/pdf/eng/2003reportmercury.pdf.

[138] CEC. Commission for Environmental Cooperation. North American Regional Action Plan on Mercury. Accessible at: www.cec.org/programs_projects/pollutants_health/smoc/merc134. cfm?varlan=english.

[139] UNECE, 1998. United Nations Economic Commission for Europe. Convention on Long-Range Transboundary Air Pollution. Protocol on Heavy Metals. Accessible at: www.unece.org/env/lrtap/hm_h1.htm.

[140] UNEP Mercury Programme. For information, see: www.chem.unep.ch/mercury/default.htm.

[141] UNEP, 2005. Results of the Governing Council's discussions on chemicals management, including mercury programme, at its 23rd session in February, 2005. Accessible at: www.chem.unep.ch/mercury/GC23-results.htm.

[142] UNEP Mercury Programme Partnerships. For information, see: www.chem.unep.ch/mercury/partnerships/default.htm.

[143] UNIDO. United Nations Industrial Development Organization. Global Mercury Project. For information, see: www.unido.org/en/doc/4571.

[144] AMAP. Arctic Monitoring and Assessment Programme. For information, see: www.amap.no/.

[145] UNEP. Basel Convention. For information, see: www.basel.int/index.html.

[146] EPA, 2000. Mercury Research Strategy. EPA-600-R-00-073. Accessible at: http://cfpub. epa.gov/ncea/cfm/recordisplay.cfm?deid=20853.

[147] EPA, 2003a. Mercury Research Multi-Year Plan. Accessible at: www.epa.gov/osp/myp/mercury.pdf.

[148] EPA. Science To Achieve Results (STAR) Program. For information, see: http://cfpub.epa. gov/ncer_abstracts/index.cfm/fuseaction/recipients.display/rfa_id/109. http://cfpub.epa.gov/ncer_abstracts/index.cfm/fuseaction/research.display/rpt/abs/rfa_id/2.

[149] USGS. The Mercury Roundtable. For information, see: http://minerals.usgs.gov/mercury/roundtable.html.

[150] EPA, 2003d. Performance and Cost of Mercury and Multipollutant Emission Control Technology Applications on Electric Utility Boilers; EPA/600/R-03/110; October, 2003. Srivastava, R.K., J.E. Staudt, and W. Jozewicz, 2004. Preliminary Estimates of Performance and Cost of Mercury Emission Control Technology Applications on Electric Utility Boilers: An Update. Prepared for presentation at The Combined Power Plant Air Pollutant Control Mega Symposium, Washington, DC, August 30–September 2, 2004.

[151] EPA, 2005a.

[152] EPA, 2005a.

[153] www.epa.gov/mercury.

[154] Revision of December 2000 Regulatory Finding on the Emissions of Hazardous Air Pollutants From Electric Utility Steam Generating Units and the Removal of Coaland Oil-Fired Electric Utility Steam Generating Units from the Section 112(c) List" (The Section 112(n) Revision Rule) (70 FR 15994 (Mar. 29, 2005) and "Standards of Performance for New and Existing Stationary Sources: Electric Utility Steam Generating Units" ("The Clean Air Mercury Rule" or "CAMR") (70 FR 28606 (May 18, 2005).

[155] Landis, M.S., R.K. Stevens, F. Shaedlich, and E.M. Presbo, 2002. Development and Characterization of an Annular Denuder Methodology for the Measurement of Divalent Inorganic Reactive Mercury in Ambient Air. Environmental Science Technology 26: 3000–3009.

[156] Bullock, R. and Brehme, K. 2002. "Atmospheric Mercury Simulation Using the CMAQ Model: Formulation, Description, and Analysis of Wet Deposition Results", Atmos. Envi., 36, pg. 2135-2146.

[157] EPA, 2003d. Srivastava, R.K., J.E. Staudt, and W. Jozewicz, 2004.

[158] EPA, 2005e. Control of Mercury Emissions from Coal-Fired Electric Utility Boilers: an Update, 02/18/05. Accessible at: www.epa.gov/ttn/atw/utility/ord_whtpaper_hgcontroltech_oar-2002-0056-6141.pdf.

[159] Kosson, D.S., H.A. van der Sloot, F. Sanchez, F. and A.C. Garrabrants, 2002. An Integrated Framework for Evaluating Leaching in Waste Management and Utilization of Secondary

Materials. Environmental Engineering Science 19(3):159–204. Thorneloe, S., 2003. Presentation to EPA Science Advisory Board, Environmental Engineering Committee, Washington, D.C., June 17, 2003. Potential for Cross-media Transfers from Management of Mercury-enriched Coal Combustion Residues. Feb. 18, 2005. Available through www.regulations.gov at EPA-HQ-OAR-2002-0056/6139.

[160] EPA. Mercury Continuous Emission Monitors. For information, see: www.epa.gov/etv/ verifications/vcenter1-11.html.

[161] Wang, Q., D. Kim, D. Dionysiou, G. Sorial and D. Timberlake, 2004. "Sources and Remediation for Mercury Contamination in Aquatic Sediments—A Literature Review," Environmental Pollution 131 (2004) 323–336. Kim, D., Q. Wang, G. Sorial, D. Dionysiou and D. Timberlake, 2004. "A Model Approach for Evaluating Effects of Remedial Actions on Mercury Speciation and Transport in a Lake System," Science of the Total Environment 327 (2004) 1–15.

[162] Randall, P.M., Chattopadhyay, S., and Ickes, J.A, 2004. Influence of pH and Oxidation-Reduction (Eh) Potential on the Dissolution of Mercury-Containing Mine Wastes from the Sulfur Bank Mercury Mine, Minerals & Metallurgical Processing Journal 21:93–98, May 2004.

[163] Randall, P.M, L. Brown, L. Deschaine, J. Dimarzio, G. Kaiser, and J. Vierow, 2004. Application of the Analytic Hierarchy Process to Compare Alternatives for the Long-Term Management of Surplus Mercury, Journal of Environmental Management 71(1):35–43. Accessible at: http://dx.doi.org/10.1016/j.jenvman.2004.01.004. Porter, S., et al., 2004. Toxic Metals in the Environment: Thermodynamic Considerations for Possible Immobilization Strategies for Pb, Cd, As, and Hg, Critical Reviews in Environmental Science and Technology, 34:395–604. EPA, 2002b. Preliminary Analysis of Alternatives for the Long Term Management of Excess Mercury. EPA/600/R-03/048. Accessible at: www.epa.gov/ORD/NRMRL/Pubs/600R03048/600R03048.html.

[164] Discussions of the fish sample data gathered by Region 8 will be included in the Human Health and Ecological Risk Assessment for the Cheyenne River Basin Site.

[165] MDN. Mercury Deposition Monitoring Network. NADP. National Air Deposition Monitoring Program. For information see: http://nadp.sws.uiuc.edu/mdn/.

[166] FDA. U.S. Food and Drug Administration. Mercury in Fish: FDA Monitoring Program. For information, see: www.cfsan.fda.gov/~frf/seamehg2.html.

[167] EPA. National Fish Tissue Study. For information, see: www.epa.gov/waterscience/fishstudy/.

[168] EPA, 2005c.

[169] Mahaffey, K.R., 2005. Exposures to Mercury in the Americas. In: Pirrone, N. and K.R. Mahaffey, Dynamics of Mercury Pollution on Regional and Global Scales. Springer-Verlag, New York.

[170] CDC. National Health and Nutrition Examination Survey, (NHANES). For information, see: www.cdc.gov/nchs/about/major/nhanes/growthcharts/charts.htm.

[171] CDC, 2003. Mercury, PP. 17-19 in Second National Report on Human Exposure to Environmental Chemicals, January 2003. Accessible at: www.cdc.gov/exposurereport/2nd/.

[172] CDC, 2004. Blood Mercury Levels in Young Children and Childbearing–Aged Women— United States, 1999–2002. Morbidity and Mortality Weekly Report, November 5, 2004/53(43):1018–1020. Accessible at: www.cdc.gov/mmwr/preview/mmwrhtml/ mm5343a5.htm.

[173] NHANES 2005-2006 Ethics Review Board Protocol. CDC, National Center for Health Statistics, Division of Health and Nutrition Examination Survey.

[174] EPA, 2003b. America's Children and the Environment: Measures of Contaminants, Body Burden, and Illness. EPA 240-R-03- 001, February 2003. Accessible at: www.epa.gov/ envirohealth/children/.

[175] EPA, 2003c. Draft Report on the Environment. Accessible at: www.epa.gov/indicators/ roe/html/roeTOC.htm.

INDEX

Q

R

S